PRENTICE HALL
LITERATURE LIBRARY

Myths and Legends From Ancient Greece and Around the World

PRENTICE HALL
Upper Saddle River, New Jersey
Needham, Massachusetts

ISBN 0-13-436033-8

1 2 3 4 5 6 7 8 9 10   02 01 00 99 98

PRENTICE HALL

Acknowledgments

Grateful acknowledgment is made to the following for copyrighted material:

Allyn & Bacon, Inc.
"The Judgement of Paris," "The Olympic Council" and "Other Important Gods" from *Myths and Their Meaning* by Max J. Herzberg. Copyright © 1984 by Allyn & Bacon, Inc. All rights reserved.

August House, Inc.
"The Hungry Goddess" from *Momentos Mágicos/Magic Moments* by Olga Loya, with Spanish translations by Carmen Lizardi-Rivera. Copyright © 1997 by Olga Loya. Reprinted by permission of August House, Inc.

Bantam Doubleday Dell Books for Young Readers
"The Trojan War" from *D'Aulaire's Book of Greek Myths* by Ingri and Edgar Parin d'Aulaire. Copyright © 1962 by Ingri and Edgar Parin d'Aulaire.

Martin Bennet
"Head Over Heart" from *West African Trickster Tales* retold by Martin Bennett. Copyright © Martin Bennett 1994.

Daisy Bates/Barbara Ker Wilson
"Joongabilbil Brings Fire", *Tales Told to Kabbarli*, University of Adelaide/Angus & Robertson, 1972.

Peter Bedrick Books, Inc.
From "Orpheus and Eurydice" and "The Wanderings of Odysseus" from *Gods, Men & Monsters from the Greek Myths* by Michael Gibson. Copyright © 1977 by Eurobook Limited. All rights reserved. Published by agreement with Eurobooks Limited, England.

Belithz Press Ltd.
"The Bridge of Magpies" and "The Deceitful Pelican" from *Folk Tales & Fables of Asia & Australia* by Robert Ingpen & Barbara Hayes. Copyright © David Bateman Ltd. & Dragon's World 1994.

(Acknowledgments continue on p. 152.)

Contents

Introduction

This collection is a key to another world—a world of superhuman deeds, heroism, love, jealousy, war, tragedy, and triumph. The tales within are metaphors for us, sharing wisdom we can use. They tell us how earlier people explained the phenomena of nature, and they offer us a glimpse into other cultures. Mostly, we look to them to help us answer the questions that have mystified people forever, ancient and modern alike. How did our world come to be? What is our place in the world—are we heroes and heroines, or are we aimless wanderers, unsure of our purpose? Answers found in this collection suggest that human beings have great promise.

MYTHS

A myth is a fictional tale that addresses questions about creation and the mysteries of nature. Different myths offer their own perspectives on how the world began. For instance, we see three views about how humans came to have knowledge of the power and use of fire in "Zeus and the Creation of Mankind," "From Bumba," and "Joongabilbil Brings Fire."

In earlier times, people needed to explain the unexplainable by having a group of powerful gods and goddesses who controlled events. Even so, it is interesting to note that the gods and goddesses had limitations. In "Daedelus" and "The Judgment of Paris," we see them brought down by jealousy; in "Perseus," "Theseus and the Minotaur," and "The Death of Balder," we learn that even the gods cannot control the stronger forces of prophecy and fate. These powerful beings show very human failings. Even while they are engaged in the important tasks of creating and maintaining the world, the gods and goddesses fight battles among themselves—and given their power, the clashes have an enormous impact upon the earth, the elements, and humans. In "The Golden Fleece" and "The Trojan War," the very future of nations is determined.

Myths have little historical truth and involve supernatural elements. Every culture has its collections of myths—from classical Greek and Roman to Native American, Indian, and Australian. Some of these myths are considered sacred today, as stories of divine beings who have been prayed to, praised, feared, loved, and worshipped.

LEGENDS

Some legends are completely fictional, but many, such as the stories of King Arthur and Hiawatha, are interwoven with the history of a people or nation. Research shows that there actually may have been an ancient King Arthur of Britain, and the American poet Henry Wadsworth Longfellow based "The Song of Hiawatha" on the life of a Mohawk chief who lived centuries ago.

Fact or fiction, most legends tell of noble, daring deeds. Reading about heroes can lift us out of our everyday lives and remind us that every person has the potential for greatness and glory. The heroism of King Arthur, the example of good overcoming evil in "The Seven Simeons," the bravery seen in "Perseus" and "Theses and the Minotaur"—these are stories that show ideal behavior that we might strive towards.

READING MYTHS AND LEGENDS

Whether past or present, near or far, as humans we are very much alike. Reading "Persephone" and "The Hungry Goddess," we see how ancient people explained how the world and the seasons were created. Even with our advances in science, we still have many unanswered questions about the universe. The poignancy of "The First People" tells of human beginnings that are characterized by difficulty and sadness, uniting us in empathy. Other stories feel especially familiar, suggesting that people from various cultures share story connections: "Brunhild" may remind us of "Sleeping Beauty"; we recognize "The Sword in the Stone" as one of our popular animated films.

There are potent lessons for us in the tales, giving us goals to aim for or warning us of perils in our path. "Hiiaka" is a moving account of loyalty and danger, describing the sacrifice sisters make for one another. "The Bridge of Magpies" stresses the positive influence love can have, even on nature itself.

Sometimes wisdom is offered with light-hearted humor, as in the trickster tales, where animals are given human qualities. "Head Over Heart, or, How Monkey Tricked Shark and So Saved His Life," a delightfully titled narrative demonstrates how, by using one's wits, the weak and good can overtake the mighty and evil.

People have preserved their myths and legends by passing them down through the generations. Why are these stories considered such a precious heritage? Perhaps it is because we possess a need to communicate with one another about our passages through life, whether they are fortunate, humorous, or treacherous. As the Indian myth, "The Broken Tusk," aptly states, there is an abiding need to tell our human story—of life and death, good and evil, war and peace.

THEMES IN THIS ANTHOLOGY

The stories in this collection are organized by theme. Among the CLASSICAL MYTHS, there are **Gods, Titans, and Origins**—"Mother Earth and Her Children," "Zeus and the Creation of Mankind," and "Persephone"; **Quests and Adventures**—"The Golden Fleece," "Chariot of the Sun God: The Story of Phaeton and Helios," and "Daedelus"; **Tales of Love and Friendship**—"Orpheus and Eurydice" and "Echo and Narcissus"; **Great Heroes**—"Perseus" and "Theseus and the Minotaur"; and **The Trojan War**—"The Judgment of Paris," "The Trojan War," "The Wanderings of Odysseus," and "The Wanderings of Aeneas".

The section on NORSE MYTHS AND MEDIEVAL LEGENDS includes **Norse Myths**—"The Death of Balder," "The Twilight of the Gods," and "Brunhild" and **The legend of King Arthur**—"The Sword in the Stone".

Finally, MYTHS FROM AROUND THE WORLD contains tales about **Origins**—"Apsu and Tiamat the Creators," "The Hungry Goddess," "The First People," "From Bumba," and "How Grandmother Spider Named the Clans"; **Gods, Goddesses, and Spirits**—"The Broken Tusk," "The Bridge of Magpies," "World Without Sun," and "Hiiaka"; **Tricksters**—"Krishna and the Serpent," "Coyote and the Blackbirds," "Head Over Heart, or, How Monkey Tricked Shark and So Saved His Life," and "The Deceitful Pelican"; and **Questing Heroes**—"The Famine," "The Creation of Night," "The Seven Simeons," and "Joongabilbil Brings Fire".

Classical Myths

The Olympic Council

Greek	Latin/Roman	Realm	Symbols
Zeus	Jupiter (Jove)	King of the gods and ruler of mankind	Eagle, oak, thunderbolts
Poseidon	Neptune	God of sea, horses, and earthquakes	Trident, dolphins, horses
Phoebus Apollo	(Same)	God of sun, music, poetry, and medicine	Lyre, arrows, sun chariot
Hermes	Mercury	Messenger of the gods, god of commerce and theft	Winged cap, winged sandals
Ares	Mars	God of war	Sword, shield, dogs, vultures
Hephaestus	Vulcan	God of fire and of workers in metal	Anvil, forge
Hera	Juno	Queen of the gods, wife of Jove, and patroness of married women	Pomegranate, peacock, cuckoo
Demeter	Ceres	Goddess of agriculture	Sheaf of wheat, poppies, cornucopia
Artemis	Diana	Goddess of moon and hunting, patroness of maidens	Crescent, stag, arrows
Pallas Athena	Minerva	Goddess of wisdom, war, and weaving	Shield, owl, shield, olive tree
Aphrodite	Venus	Goddess of love and beauty	Doves, sparrows
Hestia	Vesta	Goddess of hearth and home	Hearth fire

Other Important Gods

Greek	Latin/Roman	Realm	Symbols
Cronus	Saturn	Father of Jupiter; among the Romans, god of agriculture	Sickle
Bacchus (Dionysus)	Liber	God of wine, drama, and revelry	Ivy, grapes, leopards
Hades (Pluto)	Dis	God of the underworld, minerals, and wealth	Cerberus, cypress
Eros	Cupid	God of love	Heart pierced with arrow
Pan	Faunus	God of nature	Goats, satyrs
Eos	Aurora	Goddess of the dawn	Torch, large wings, horse-drawn chariot

Mother Earth and Her Children

by Alice Low

IN the very beginning, there was no earth or sea or sky. There was only a mass of confusion in darkness, called Chaos.

After many, many years, Mother Earth, named Gaea, was born out of Chaos. And after many more years, she gave birth to a son, Uranus, who was Father Heaven.

Father Heaven loved Mother Earth, and he made rain fall on her, so that flowers and trees and grass grew. The rain also fell into hollows and crevices, forming seas and rivers and lakes. Then Mother Earth created many kinds of animals to live in the forests and fields and oceans and lakes.

Mother Earth and Father Heaven had many children. First Mother Earth gave birth to three monstrous sons, each with fifty heads and one hundred hands. Then she gave birth to three more gigantic sons, just as ugly, called the Cyclopes. Each Cyclops had only one eye right in the middle of his forehead. These six sons were as strong as earthquakes and tornados put together. And they were often as destructive.

Finally Mother Earth bore the first gods, six sons and six daughters called the Titans. They, too, were gigantic, yet somewhat more like humans than her first children. They were just as strong as her first six sons, but sometimes they used their power wisely.

Father Heaven could not stand the sight of his first six ugly sons, and he was afraid of them, too. One day he threw them into a dark hole under the earth.

Mother Earth cried bitterly over this cruelty to her children. She decided to destroy Father Heaven and bring back her beloved children. She made a weapon, a sickle, and gave it to the Titans. "Kill your cruel father," she begged them, "and then go down into that dark hole and bring your brothers back to me."

Cronus, the strongest and bravest of the Titans, led the attack on his father and wounded him dreadfully. Then he released his brothers. The Titans made Cronus the ruler of heaven and earth and their sister, Rhea, his wife and queen.

But power changed Cronus, and now *he* imprisoned his brothers, the one-eyed Cyclopes and the hundred-handed monsters, in that dark hole under the earth.

This enraged Mother Earth, but she did not tell Cronus how she felt. She bided her time while Cronus's wife, Rhea, bore sons, for she knew that one of them was destined to overthrow Cronus.

Cronus, too, knew that one of his children was to rise up against him and take his place as king of the gods. Therefore, to keep his children from growing up and becoming powerful, he swallowed them as soon as they were born.

Rhea was deeply saddened as, one by one, Cronus devoured her first five children: Hestia, Demeter, Hera, Hades, and Poseidon. When she was expecting her sixth child, she determined to save it from Cronus. After her baby son, Zeus, was born, she gave him to Mother Earth, who hid the baby in a cave on the island of Crete.

Then Rhea went to Cronus and said, "Here is our sixth child, a son. Do whatever you wish with him." She handed Cronus a bundle that looked like a baby wrapped in a blanket.

Of course Cronus swallowed it, just as Rhea had expected. But Cronus had swallowed a stone wrapped in a blanket, not the baby Zeus.

Now Rhea was happy. She hoped that Zeus was the son who would destroy his frightful father, Cronus.

Zeus grew up on Crete among shepherds and nymphs, far from his wicked father, Cronus. He drank the milk of a goat nymph, who fed him honey, too. He slept in a golden cradle that was hung from a tree, and armed guards protected him. Whenever he cried, the guards banged their spears on their shields so that Cronus would not hear Zeus's loud wails and know that he still lived.

Nevertheless Cronus learned that his son was alive on Crete, and he went after him, intending to swallow him. But Zeus was too clever for Cronus. He changed himself into a serpent, and though Cronus searched high and low, he could not find Zeus.

Rhea, Zeus's mother, had told him about the terrible deeds of his father, and Zeus vowed that when he was fully grown, he would rescue his brothers and sisters.

At last that time came. Zeus returned to Rhea and disguised himself as a servant in Cronus's palace. Then he and Rhea laid their plot. "If you will concoct a poisonous potion," said Zeus to his mother, "I will mix it into Cronus's drink." His mother agreed readily, and when the poisoned drink had been prepared, Zeus served it to Cronus. Cronus drank it quickly, for he was thirsty.

He became very ill and vomited up the stone he had swallowed. The pains continued as, one by one, out of Cronus's mouth sprang his five children.

Zeus's brothers and sisters hugged him and thanked him for giving them new life. "And now that you have set us free," they said to Zeus, "you must lead us in a battle against Cronus and the Titans. We, not they, must rule the universe, and never again will we be imprisoned."

The terrible war raged for ten long years. Cronus was no longer young, so Atlas led the Titans. However, two other Titans, Prometheus and Epimetheus, joined Zeus and his brothers and sisters. That made the two sides nearly equal in strength. Neither could win.

Finally wise Mother Earth told Zeus that his side would be victorious if he followed her advice. "Go down into the dark hole under the earth and release the one-eyed Cyclopes and their hundred-handed brothers, for they shall help you win."

Zeus followed Mother Earth's advice and descended bravely into the dark hole. He killed the guard and freed the prisoners. Then he gave them divine food and drink, and at last their strength returned.

The Cyclopes, in turn, gave Zeus gifts to use as weapons against Cronus and the Titans.

"To Zeus," said one of the Cyclopes, "we give our powerful weapons, the thunderbolts."

"To Zeus's brother Hades," said another, "we give this magic helmet of darkness."

"And to their brother Poseidon," said the third, "we give this sharp-pronged trident."

Zeus and Hades and Poseidon thanked the Cyclopes and discussed how best to use their gifts.

Then Hades put on his helmet of darkness, which made him invisible. He crept up behind Cronus and stole his weapons.

Poseidon struck the ground with his trident, which caused the earth to shake. Cronus, terrified, became powerless.

Then Zeus threw his thunderbolts, and Cronus and Atlas and the rest of the Titans retreated.

Meanwhile the three hundred-handed brothers hurled three hundred rocks at the Titans, all at once, over and over.

The earth was almost torn apart by the dreadful battle, but before it could be destroyed, Zeus and his brothers and sisters won. They punished all the Titans except for Prometheus and

Epimetheus, who had helped them. They made Atlas, the Titans' leader, carry the whole sky on his shoulders, forever. And they chained Cronus and the others in the dark hole under the earth.

Zeus could not rest long, though, for Mother Earth gave birth to one more enemy, the most terrible of all, a monster named Typhon. Typhon had one hundred heads and spurted a stream of fire from each eye. But Zeus hurled his thunderbolts and struck down that hideous creature. At last there was peace on earth.

Now, which of the three brothers, Zeus, Poseidon, or Hades, should be the ruler of the universe? They had had enough fighting, and they wanted to settle this problem without an argument.

They decided to draw lots. Hades won the underworld, and Poseidon won the sea. And Zeus became lord of heaven and ruler of all the gods of Mount Olympus.

Zeus and the Creation of Mankind

by Alice Low

WHEN it was time for man to be created, Zeus gave this important work to Prometheus and Epimetheus, the two Titans who had helped him in his battle against Cronus and the other Titans. Zeus also assigned them the task of giving men and animals gifts that would insure their survival.

Prometheus, whose name means "forethought," was an inventor and exceedingly wise. His brother, Epimetheus, whose name means "afterthought," was just the opposite, exceedingly rash.

Epimetheus decided that *he* would give the gifts to the animals, and Prometheus set about creating the first man. He wanted man to be nobler than the animals, and he sat by the ocean for a long time, thinking. Finally he took a handful of earth and added water to it, so that it would hold together when he shaped it. Then, slowly and carefully, he modeled the first man in the image of the gods. Prometheus gave him two feet on which to stand, so that he could look up to heaven and the stars, not down at the earth as the animals did.

Meanwhile Epimetheus was handing out gifts to the animals, which, until that time, had had no means of defense and looked very different from the way they do today. Epimetheus gave claws to the tigers, wings to the birds, and horns to the cattle. And then he gave some of the animals swiftness, others cunning and courage, and still others strength. He even gave many of them fur to keep them warm in winter.

Epimetheus was very pleased with himself. But then Prometheus ran up to him, shouting, "Look, brother. My man has come to life. Is he not wonderful? Let us give the greatest gift to him, for he is by far the finest creation on earth."

Epimetheus hung his head and said, "But I have already given all of the greatest gifts to the animals. I am sorry, brother. I did not stop to think."

When Prometheus heard what his brother had done, he was angry. "Now there is nothing precious to give to man. I must think of some superior and special gift to help man survive."

Prometheus was quick-witted, and soon he thought of a remarkable gift—fire! With fire man could keep warm, cook food, and have light at night. He could also forge tools to plow the earth, and weapons to defend himself against animals. But how was Prometheus to obtain fire, which belonged only to the gods?

He asked the goddess Athena to help him gain entrance to heaven, and she guided him to the blazing chariot of the sun. There Prometheus lighted a torch and then, unseen, sped back to earth to give his precious gift to mankind.

Zeus was enraged when he looked down at the earth and saw fires glowing. "Prometheus has stolen fire, which belongs to the gods alone," he roared. "And he has given our fire to man! It may make man too powerful, more powerful even than the gods. I must punish Prometheus."

Zeus acted swiftly. He had his servants Force and Violence seize Prometheus and chain him to a rock, high in the Caucasus Mountains. There, day after day, a vulture swooped down and ate his liver, which grew back daily, only to be eaten again.

But Prometheus suffered in silence, for though his body was bound, his mind and spirit were free. He did not regret his deed. He knew that not only had he fashioned a wonderful creation—man—but he also had given him a gift that would change him from a helpless creature to master of his surroundings.

Persephone

by Ann Pilling

AT the beginning of time, when the gods defeated the giants, the world was divided into three by the casting of lots. Zeus won the sky, and his brother Poseidon the sea. The underworld was left to Hades. He was a brooding, lonely god, and he begged Zeus to give him a wife from the land above. He had fallen in love with Persephone, the daughter of Demeter.

Demeter was the most powerful of all the goddesses; she ruled over every living thing on earth, and without her nothing would grow. Zeus knew that she would never agree to let her daughter marry Hades, and he feared her anger if he dared ask such a question. But the king of the underworld was determined that Persephone would be his wife, and he decided to carry her off by force.

For many days he waited and watched. Then, one morning, he heard that she was out in the meadows on the slopes of Mount Etna, picking flowers with the Daughters of Ocean. These nymphs were very beautiful, but none of them so beautiful as the radiant Persephone. She outshone them as day outshines night.

Zeus had conspired with Hades to help him trap her, and now, at her feet, she saw a most marvelous plant appear from nowhere. It was a white narcissus with a hundred flowers growing from its root, a thing so lovely and so fragrant that not only mortals but the gods themselves wondered at it.

Persephone bent down to pick the flower. But, as her fingers closed on it, the mountain split open with a terrible roaring noise, and from the depths came Hades riding on his black chariot, pulled by huge black horses. With a cry of triumph he swept the terrified Persephone up into the chariot and galloped away, down to the underworld.

Two others knew about this cruel thing. One was old Hecate, the witch goddess, who had heard how the girl cried out in terror. The other was Helios, god of the sun, who had seen the enormous black chariot rise up from the gash in the earth, and the greedy fingers of Hades, snatching the girl away. But he was driving his sun horses across the sky and could not cease in his labors until the day was done.

Demeter also heard the echo of her daughter's voice, from far away, on Mount Parthenia, and she set off at once to find her, wandering over the earth, not stopping to eat or drink, and taking no rest. On the ninth day she met old Hecate, who told her she had heard the girl cry out on Mount Etna. Then she met Helios, who confessed that he too knew what had happened, and that Zeus had plotted to help his brother Hades by setting the white flower at Persephone's feet.

When she heard this, Demeter's grief turned to rage. She left Mount Olympus, where the gods lived, disguised herself as an old woman, and went to Eleusis, where she built a temple and spent long days there, mourning and weeping for her lost daughter.

And she turned her back upon the earth and all that she must do there to make things grow. For a whole year the land sent up no shoots, and cattle pulled plows across the fields in vain. The white barley seed fell useless from the sower's hand and rotted where it lay.

People began to starve, and in alarm Zeus sent Iris, the goddess of the rainbow, down to earth to plead for mercy from the goddess of grain. But Demeter refused to listen to her, nor would she listen to Zeus's other messengers. Day after day she sat alone in her temple at Eleusis, vowing that she would never return to Olympus, or allow any green thing to grow upon earth, until Persephone was restored to her.

At last Zeus sent his own son, Hermes, to plead with the god of the underworld. He knew the way well, for it was his task to lead the dead from earth down to hell. Sadfaced, he stood before Hades' throne, having taken off his winged sandals and set aside the gold rod with which he pointed the way. And the tragic Persephone, so small on her great black throne, listened in silence as he pleaded with her husband.

"Great Hades," he said. "Upon earth people are dying because Demeter has put a curse on all her crops. Release Persephone, I beg you. If you do not, Zeus will soon have no subjects to rule over. This kingdom too will die, for the world will be empty." And the tears ran down his face.

Hades thought for a moment, then rose, and put his queen's hand into that of Hermes. "Go," he said, "since Zeus commands it. But do not forget me, Persephone. I have been kind to you. Remember too that all the souls here remain your subjects, wherever you may be." And he turned away sadly, into his dark kingdom.

So they returned joyously to earth, and Persephone was restored to her mother's arms. But then the goddess drew back, for the stain of a fruit was upon the girl's mouth. "Did you eat in the underworld?" she asked fearfully.

"Only a few seeds from a pomegranate," answered the innocent Persephone. Then Demeter knew that Hades had tricked them, for whoever eats food in the kingdom of the dead cannot ever escape from it.

So Zeus made a pact with his brother, and for three months of the year Persephone has to live with her dark king, under the earth. In those short, hard days, nothing grows upon earth. Demeter mourns for her daughter in a dress of frost and snow.

When the girl is restored to her, Demeter's heart grows light again. Spring comes, and blossoms. After this the summer opens out in glory, and then the rich harvest appears. Only when Hades claims his queen again does the year begin to sicken and die.

Then people remember Persephone, and they remember too that the dark and cold are only for a season and that the winter woods always contain the promise of a new spring.

The Golden Fleece

retold by Anne Terry White

JASON was the rightful heir to the throne of Iolcus, but there seemed little chance that he would ever sit upon it. For his uncle Pelias had seized it and driven Jason's father away. The boy himself had been brought up by the centaur Chiron. This kindly creature, who was half-horse, half-man, had educated many heroes in his cave. Under his care Jason learned all that befits a stalwart man to know.

Now Pelias, the false king, was troubled by a strange oracle. He had been told to beware of a man wearing but one sandal. Pelias turned the mysterious words over and over in his mind, but could make nothing of them. And he was still worrying about the meaning years later, when Jason, his nephew, decided to travel to Iolcus and assert his rights.

Jason had grown into a tall, handsome man, and as he journeyed along, none could help admiring him. His bright, unshorn locks hung down his neck. The skin of a leopard he had strangled was thrown over his close-fitting leather tunic. Two broadbladed spears were in his hand. He looked so much like a god that many he met wondered whether he might not be one of the immortals.

As he approached the city of Iolcus, Jason had to cross a muddy river, and in crossing it he lost his sandal in the mud. So he arrived in the market place of the capital wearing but one. The place was thronged, for the King was just then making a sacrifice.

"Who can that be?" the people said to one another, looking at the handsome stranger with wonder. "Is this perhaps Apollo come in disguise?"

But the King's eyes went—as ever they did—to the stranger's feet. He saw but one sandal, and his face paled and his heart all but stood still.

"Who are you and what is your father's name?" the King asked when the rites were finished.

"I am Jason, the son of King Aeson," the young man replied. "And I have come to visit my father's house."

Pelias hid his fears under courteous words and invited Jason into the palace, where he entertained his nephew royally for five days. Then Jason said to him in a matter-of-fact way:

"This kingdom is mine for I am the rightful heir. But I shall leave you the wealth you took from my father. All the fields and the herds shall be yours. I ask only the scepter and throne which were my father's."

Pelias thought fast, and his face changed color several times as he spoke.

"All shall be as you wish," he said. "But I, too, have a request to make. I have been troubled by a dream. The shade of Phrixus has appeared to me. He has implored me to bring back to Greece the golden fleece of that sacred ram which once carried him across the sea to Colchis and which afterwards he sacrificed to Zeus. Go you in my stead. Bring back to Greece that glorious prize and put the spirit of Phrixus at rest."

When Jason heard these words, his soul was mightily stirred. For the golden fleece was the great prize of which every hero in Greece dreamed. All knew that in the land of Colchis the golden fleece hung from an oak in a sacred grove, where an unsleeping dragon guarded it by day and by night. Jason's mind and heart were instantly so filled with longing for it that he did not stop to examine his wily uncle's reasons for proposing the adventure to him.

"I will go to Colchis with a band of heroes," he agreed at once. "And I will set the soul of Phrixus at ease."

Thereupon Jason sent heralds to all the courts of Greece, calling for bold men who dared to sail with him. And he had Argus the Thespian build him a fifty-oared ship.

Hero after hero answered the call. Argus himself volunteered to go, he who had built the vessel. Heracles of Tiryns, the strongest man who ever lived, joined Jason. Laertes, grandson of Zeus, who one day would be father of Odysseus of the many adventures, came from Argos. Orpheus, the poet and wondrous musician who descended into Hades to seek his dead wife, Eurydice, hastened from Thrace. Peleus, who would one day father Achilles, the great hero of the Trojan War, also came. And many others of glittering fame hastened to Iolcus, so that never before had so gallant a ship's company come together.

When all was ready, Jason made a solemn offering to the gods of the sea. The heroes took their seats at the oars, and the *Argo* weighed anchor. Dangers untold lay before the bold Argonauts. But not one of the heroes lost heart.

Who can tell of all that happened before the Argonauts reached Colchis? It would take many books to say the whole, for countless men have recorded the adventures of the heroes, and each tells the story in his own way. But arrive at last they did. It was sunset, and they were weary. They took down their sails, then rowed up the river toward the capital, and made the vessel fast. With a grateful heart, Jason offered up a libation to the gods. Then, filled with uncertainty about the morrow, the heroes lay down to rest.

"My plan," said Jason next morning when the heroes consulted together, "is to get the golden fleece without fighting, if possible. I shall ask King Aeetes for it, and from his own mouth we shall learn what course we must take. Now remain quietly here on the ship, my noble comrades, while I with two of your number will go to the palace."

King Aeetes received the Argonauts graciously. According to custom, he asked no questions until they were sitting down to food. But he no sooner learned who they were and what their errand was than his manner changed.

"Not for the golden fleece but to take my scepter and my throne you have come!" he broke out in fury. "Return to your homes before I have your tongues cut out and your hands lopped off!"

"Restrain your anger, King Aeetes," Jason answered courteously. "We have come for no other purpose than I have stated. Destiny and the command of a wicked king prompted me to come. I pray you, grant our request. Give us the golden fleece. And if there is any service we can render you as fighting men, we shall gladly do it."

The King frowned. Then, changing his manner, he spoke more mildly.

"I hold no grudge against brave men," he said. "But you must prove your courage. In the field of Ares I have two bulls whose feet are of bronze and whose breath is fire. You must yoke them and plow that field. Instead of grain, you must sow dragon's teeth. From them a crop of warriors will spring up. These you must slay before nightfall. All this I have done myself. If you cannot do it, I will not give up the fleece, for it is but just that the more valiant man shall have it."

Jason sat speechless and confused. How could he promise to perform such a hopeless task? At last he said:

"The labor which you ask is heavy. But I will undertake it— even though I perish in the attempt. There are worse things than death."

With this the Argonauts rose from the table and went back to their ship.

When the rest of the comrades heard what a fearful task Aeetes had set Jason, many offered to undertake the trial in his stead. But he refused them all.

"My destiny has brought me here," he said, "and come what may, I will obey it."

But now there came to them one of the King's grandsons, Argus by name, whom Jason had by chance once rescued from a wrecked ship.

"Jason," he said, "there is no hope of your performing the labor my grandfather has set you. Let me, therefore, seek the help of Medea. She is my mother's young sister, and is a maiden skilled in brewing magic potions. Hecate herself, whose priestess she is, has taught her. She alone can enable you to yoke the fiery bulls and plow the fields of Ares."

"We are indeed in a sad plight if our safety depends on a woman," Jason answered him sadly. "But go to her if you like. I will not hinder you."

Unknown to either Jason or Argus, Medea was herself thinking hard how she might help the hero. For she had seen Jason as he sat at her father's table and had been stirred by his beauty and manliness. Never before had she felt love for a man, but now her feelings strove against one another and were stronger than herself. Many thoughts flew through her mind. Reason said one thing, her heart another.

"If I do not help him, this noble stranger will surely perish," she said to herself. "But shall I, then, betray my father's kingdom and rescue an unknown foreigner that he may go home and become another woman's husband? Ah, but he will not do that. Before I help him he will give me his promise to marry me. He will never deceive me or forget what I have done for him."

As she sat thus thinking, her sister came to her. "Medea," she said, "my son Argus, whose life you know Jason saved, has sent me to beg your help. Give the stranger some device, I pray, whereby he can overcome the bulls."

Medea's heart laughed when she heard her sister speak, but she hid her joy.

"I will do it," she said, "only for your son Argus' sake. Let him inform Jason that early in the morning I will go to Hecate's temple and there give him the magic with which he can survive the trial with the bulls."

So Jason came to Medea in the temple of Hecate. Never had he looked so handsome. When Medea's eyes rested on the stranger from Greece, she could not take them away. And when Jason took her hand, her heart fluttered so that she was speechless. For a long time they stood silent. Then Jason said:

"Lady, I come to beg you for the charm you promised. Ask in return what you will. And know that if you enable me and my companions to go home with the golden fleece, your glory will be undying. All Greece will praise you forever."

Medea did not answer—the tumult in her breast would not let her speak. She only placed a small box in Jason's hands. He stood holding the box tightly and gazing into her eyes, as much confused as she.

At last Medea spoke. "This is what you must do," she said, and told him what mystic rites he must perform and how to use the charm she had given him.

"Salve your body with this ointment," she said, "and also your weapons, that they be not consumed by fire. And when the warriors spring from the dragon's teeth, throw a great stone in their midst. That will cause them to turn one on another. And when all of them are dead, you can take the golden fleece and depart."

Tears gushed from Medea's eyes and rolled down her beautiful face as she said the last words and added, "Do not forget the name of Medea when you come home rejoicing, for she will be thinking of you."

"Never will I forget you, noble princess," Jason said passionately, "neither by night nor by day. But if you will come with me, all the men and women of Greece will adore you, for only because of you will their sons and husbands and brothers have returned home safe. And then nothing but death should stand between us."

Medea could have listened to his words without end, but the time had come to part. So, while Jason returned to his companions, she went back to the palace to struggle with her thoughts of loyalty and home and love.

It was scarcely dawn the next day when the townspeople assembled in the sacred field of Ares. They took their stand on the upper slopes. And in their midst King Aeetes sat clad in purple, his ivory scepter in his hand. All eyes were on Jason, who stood upon the field examining the heavy yoke and plow.

Suddenly there was the sound of snorting and bellowing. Into the field rushed the brazen-footed bulls, wreathed in smoke and blowing fire from their mouths and nostrils. At the touch of their hot breath, the grass blazed up and roared as a furnace roars when it is stoked. Yet Jason went toward them. The creatures saw him and swung their awful heads from side to side. They bellowed and pawed the ground with their heavy cloven hoofs.

Rigid and breathless, the Argonauts watched from the slope as Jason boldly approached. Their hearts all but stood still when they saw Jason force first one bull, then the other, to its knees and harness the beasts to the yoke. And when the plow bit into the earth and turned up a black furrow, they broke into loud cheers, while all the Colchians stood amazed.

Jason plowed, and as he walked up the field and down, he kept taking from his helmet the dragon's teeth which had been given him and sowing them in the furrow. In the afternoon the four-acre field was done. Then Jason unyoked the bulls, and at his cry they fled in terror to their underground stable. When he turned, the crop of armed men was springing from the earth.

And now fear again took hold of the Argonauts, for they saw all the warriors prepare to hurl their spears at the hero. Even Medea felt a wave of panic surge over her as she beheld one solitary youth against so many men. Softly she chanted a spell to help him. But there was no need. Jason took up a great round stone and tossed it in the midst of the warriors, and immediately they turned on one another. To the last man they perished in that bloody war.

Then the Argonauts cheered so that the hills rang with the sound. Rushing down into the field, they hugged Jason in eager embraces. Even the Colchians shouted. But King Aeetes returned to the palace without a word. Anger gnawed at his heart. He knew that Jason could never have performed the labor without Medea's help, and he brooded into the night on vengeance and how he might outwit the clever Argonaut.

Medea passed the night in agony. She feared her father, but she also feared what might befall her if she fled with Jason. At last she made her decision. The palace doors opened at her magic spells, and she hurried to the shore where the Argonauts kept a great fire burning. At her call Jason leaped ashore.

"My father is planning fearful vengeance," Medea said. "Save yourselves and me from his wrath. I will get you the golden fleece. Only swear to me, swear that you will treat me honorably when I am a stranger in your native land."

"The gods be my witness that I shall make you my wife!" Jason promised.

"Then let us go at once and take the fleece," Medea said.

Quickly the ship carried them to the sacred grove, and together Jason and Medea approached the sacred oak. The dragon
stretched his long neck toward them. He hissed fiercely. But
Medea's charms lulled the creature to sleep, and for the first
time the sleepless eyes closed. Then Jason snatched the golden
fleece from the limb, and the two ran toward the ship.

With what wonder the Argonauts viewed the marvelous prize
they had come so far to seek! But Jason, eager to depart, would
not take time to let each man touch it.

"My noble comrades," he said, "let us be on our way, for we
shall surely be pursued. And as for Medea here, know all of you
that she who has helped us accomplish what we undertook shall
be my lawful wife. I look to you to help me protect her, for she
has rescued Greece."

So the Argonauts seated themselves hastily at the oars, and the
vessel glided down the river and out upon the waves of the sea.

Chariot of the Sun God:
The Story of Phaeton and Helios

retold by Mary Pope Osborne

PHAETON entered the gleaming palace of the sun god and walked to the throne room. He stopped in the doorway, blinded by the radiance of Helios, the sun god, who wore a purple robe and sat high on a throne of emeralds. Around Helios stood his attendants, whose names were Day, Month, Year, Century, Hours, Spring, Summer, Autumn, and Winter.

"Come to me, my boy," said Helios, the sun god.

Phaeton stepped forward and bowed his head to shield his eyes from the sun's awesome brightness. Then he kneeled before the throne.

"What brings you to seek your father?" Helios asked gently.

"I came to get your promise that I am really your son," Phaeton answered. "The boys at school laugh at me and say I'm not, but my mother has always said my father is the sun."

"Clymene is right," said Helios. "The nymph Clymene had a child by me, and it was you. To prove I'm your father, I'll give you anything you ask. I swear it by Styx, the river of oaths."

"Father, I've only one wish. I want to do what you do early each morning. I want to drive your fiery chariot alone across the sky and turn night into day."

"Oh, no! I cannot allow you to do that!" cried Helios.

"But you promised—"

"I spoke too rashly! Please, may the gods allow me to take back my promise!"

"It's too late, Father!" said Phaeton.

"But this is the one wish I cannot grant, my son! The trip is too dangerous. Even Jupiter—greatest of all the gods—cannot drive my winged horses! They're hot with fire!"

"I can drive them, Father. If I'm really your son."

"No! You can't! How can you fight the spin of the world? How can you fight the wild beasts and the terrible monsters?"

But Phaeton only smiled at Helios. "I know I can do what you do, Father," he said.

The sun god tried to stall for time, but the goddess Dawn was coming quickly upon the palace, getting ready to throw open her crimson doors and to shine forth. The moon's thin crescent had vanished from sight; the stars had taken flight. It was time for Helios's fiery chariot to begin its daily course across the sky.

Helios and Phaeton stepped into the cool air where the chariot waited. The gleaming cart had tires of gold and spokes of silver, and every jewel imaginable sparkled in the rosy light of the early morning.

As Phaeton walked around the golden chariot, marveling at its beauty, his father tried to think of ways to stop him from taking the terrible journey across the sky.

But when birds began singing, Phaeton cried, "I must leave now, Father!" And he jumped into the shining chariot.

The four winged horses stamped their hooves and breathed fire from their nostrils as two goddesses, both named Hours, fastened their jingling harnesses.

The sun god rubbed a magic salve on Phaeton's face to shield him from the heat. He set his crown of flashing sunbeams on the boy's head. Then he looked at his son and sighed. "At least listen to my advice," he said. "Keep to the middle path. Do not veer off to the side! Neither get too high nor too low, for the sky and earth need equal heat. If you're too high, you'll burn the sky, and if you're too low, you'll burn the earth—"

"All right, Father!" cried Phaeton as he held the reins proudly, and the horses neighed and pawed the ground.

"Follow the wheel tracks of my daily path!" cried Helios. "Spare the whip and hold the reins tightly!"

"I will, Father! I will!"

"And beware of the northern bear and the twisting snake in the sky—"

Before the sun god could say more, Phaeton snapped the reins. "It's time, Father!" he said. "Day's calling! Night is gone!"

Suddenly the four horses leapt forward into the boundless sky.

"Don't go, my son!" shouted Helios. "Let *me* give the world light today!"

But Phaeton couldn't hear his father. The swift hooves of his horses ripped open the clouds. Then the winged steeds soared higher and higher into the sky.

The chariot was so light, it tossed back and forth like a ship on stormy waves. The horses grew frightened and galloped faster—until they were more swift than the East Wind. Phaeton pulled hard on the reins, but he couldn't slow his horses down. He looked around wildly, but he couldn't see the wheel tracks— the horses had left their worn path!

As he wheeled off course, Phaeton's sunbeams warmed the constellations: The Snake stirred from its icy numbness. The Great Bear woke in a rage and began lumbering about the heavens.

Phaeton looked below, and when he realized how far away the earth was, he became sick with fright. He called in panic for his father's help. He yelled for his horses to stop, but the horses galloped out of control. They swept past more savage beasts in the sky—past the giant scorpion that sweated black venom as its curved stinger reached out toward the fiery chariot.

Phaeton dropped the reins, and the horses bounded into regions they'd never traveled before. They crashed into stars. All of heaven cried out in terror as the fiery chariot careened off course. The moon, the skies, and the earth all caught fire. Flames spread across mountaintops and burned the snow, spilling black smoke into the clouds. Even Mount Olympus, home of the gods, was besieged with fire.

Then Phaeton saw the earth set aflame. Everything glowed white-hot: the deserts, woodland pools, and springs. Everyone on earth was trying to escape the great fire. The gods of the underworld and even the sea nymphs in their deep ocean caves felt the searing heat.

Mother Earth shielded her hot forehead and shuddered in agony. Burdened with flame, she cried out to Jupiter, the greatest of the gods: "Hurl your lightning bolts now and end this fiery death caused by Phaeton!" Then she could speak no longer, for the smoke and flames were choking her.

Jupiter, hypnotized by the sight of flames licking the world, roused himself when he saw Mother Earth dying. He rolled his thunder, then lifted a giant bolt of lightning behind his head and flung it through the sky. The bolt struck the sun chariot, breaking its wheel and spokes—and fire extinguished fire, flame put out flame, and the mad horses leapt free of their harnesses as Phaeton fell from the sky.

Phaeton's hair was on fire as he fell. Leaving behind a trail of sparks, he looked like a falling star. Far from home, half a world away from his mother, he fell into a river.

The river god held Phaeton's poor, smoldering body and bathed his burning face. Then the water nymphs buried Phaeton; and on his tomb, they wrote:

"Here lies Phaeton who tried to be the sun.
Greatly he failed, but greatly he dared."

For a whole day the sun god mourned his son. He refused to drive his chariot—and the men and women on earth had to burn fires to gain light and warmth.

When Jupiter went to see the sun god, he found him sitting on his emerald throne with his head bowed, not moving as he sat in mourning. Jupiter bid Helios to look up and answer to him for not driving his golden chariot.

But Helios cursed the god of the skies for throwing his thunderbolt and killing Phaeton.

"I had no choice!" said mighty Jupiter. "The boy's ambition nearly ended the world. Mother Earth was burning and dying. But now she is too cold, Helios. She needs your heat, or she will die from freezing."

The sun god bowed his head further.

"Rise, Helios!" roared Jupiter. "Stop blaming me for your son's death! You have work to do! The world is waiting for you!"

The sun god heaved a great sigh, then slowly rose from his throne. Trembling with sorrow, he strode out of his palace.

The four winged horses who had leapt free from Phaeton were snuffling in the cool early air, stamping their hooves as Dawn opened her crimson doors.

The sun god stepped into the gleaming golden chariot. He put on his crown of flashing sunbeams—the same crown Phaeton had worn. Then the two goddesses of Hours yoked the four winged horses with jingling harnesses. And as the weeping sun god grabbed the reins tightly and snapped them, they bolted into the boundless, blue, sunlit sky.

Daedalus

retold by Anne Terry White

IN the days when King Minos ruled Crete and his mighty navy ranged the seas, there lived in Athens a man by the name of Daedalus. And his name was known as far and wide as that of Minos. For Daedalus was the greatest architect and sculptor of his time. There was nothing his ingenious mind could not design or his skillful hands execute. And his statues were so real that people said they lived. It seemed that at any moment they might move a hand or take a step or open their lips and speak.

His young nephew, Talus, also had clever hands and a creative mind. So his mother placed him with her brother that the boy might learn his marvelous skills. But Talus had a genius of his own and even more imagination. Walking on the shore one day, he picked up the backbone of a fish. Idly he drew the strong, sharp spines forward and back across a piece of driftwood. They cut deep into the wood. He went home and notched a metal blade all along one edge—and he had a saw. Another time he fixed two iron rods together at the tip. He held one firmly upright against the earth and moved the other slowly around. It made a perfect circle—he had invented the compass.

Talus was a pupil to make any teacher excited and proud. But not Daedalus. Instead of being pleased, he was frightened and sorely jealous.

"Talus will soon surpass me!" he thought.

He could not bear the idea of a rival, and came to hate the boy. And one day, when they stood together on a height, Daedalus pushed Talus off to his death.

He had not planned the deed. It had been a sudden, crazy impulse. The next instant, horrified at what he had done, he rushed down to the boy. But it was too late. Talus was dead, and not all the wonderful skills of Daedalus could call him back. Clearly, if Daedalus wished to save his own life, he must flee. So he left Athens and wandered miserably from place to place, until at last he left Greece altogether and crossed the sea to Crete.

King Minos was delighted to have the Athenian in his realm. The King had something in mind that called for the genius of Daedalus. Minos possessed a fearful monster, with the head and shoulders of a bull and the legs and trunk of a man. The creature was called the Minotaur—that is, the Bull of Minos. The King wanted a suitable place to keep the Minotaur. The building must be such that neither the monster himself nor any victim sent in to be devoured by him could possibly escape from it.

So, at the King's command, Daedalus designed the Labyrinth. The building was a bewildering maze of passages. They turned back upon themselves, crisscrossed, and went round and round without leading anywhere. Once inside the Labyrinth, it was all but impossible to find the way out again. Even Daedalus himself was once nearly lost.

King Minos was delighted with Daedalus' work and held him in highest favor. Yet Daedalus was less than pleased, for he felt himself to be no better than a prisoner in Crete. The King was so afraid Daedalus would reveal the secret of the Labyrinth that he would not let him leave the island. And for that very reason Daedalus yearned to go. With what envy he watched the birds winging their way through the sky!

One day, as his eyes followed the graceful sea birds cleaving the ocean of air, an idea came to him.

"King Minos may shut my way out by land and by sea," he thought, "but he does not control the air."

And he began to study the flight of birds and to observe how their wings are fashioned. He watched the little song birds fold and unfold their wings, watched how they rose from ground, flew down from the trees, and went to and fro. He also watched the herons slowly flapping their great wings. He watched the eagles soar and swoop. He saw, too, how their feathers overlapped one another—where they were large and where they were small.

When he thought he understood the secrets of flight, Daedalus went to a nesting place he knew of and gathered feathers of various sizes. And in a chamber close to the roof he began to build wings. First he laid down a row of the tiniest feathers, then a row of larger ones overlapping them, and yet larger ones beyond these. He fastened the feathers together in the middle with thread and at the bottom with wax. And when he had built on enough rows, he bent them around into a gentle curve to look like real birds' wings.

His young son Icarus stood by and watched his father work. Laughing, the boy caught the feathers when they blew away in the wind. He pressed his thumb into the yellow wax to soften it for his father, hindering more than he helped.

When Daedalus had finished the pair of wings, he put them on. He raised himself in the air and hovered there. He moved

the wings just as he had seen birds do, and lo! he could fly.
Icarus clapped his hands together in delight.

"Make me a pair of wings, too, father!" he cried.

Then Daedalus made a second pair of wings and prepared his
son to fly.

"Now I warn you, Icarus," Daedalus said, "not to be reckless.
Be wise, not bold. Take a course midway between heaven and
earth. For if you fly too high, the sun will scorch your feathers.
And if you fly too low, the sea will wet them. Take me for your
guide. Follow me and you will be safe."

All the time he was speaking, Daedalus was fastening the
wings to his son's shoulders. His hands trembled as he thought
of the great adventure before them. At the same time, he was
worried about the boy. He did not know whether he could quite
trust Icarus to obey. As he adjusted his own wings and kissed
the excited child, tears ran down Daedalus' face.

"Remember," he repeated for the last time. "Heed my words
and stay close to me!"

Then he rose on his wings and flew from the housetop. Icarus
followed.

Daedalus kept a watchful eye on the boy, even as a mother
bird does when she has brought a fledgling out of its nest in the
treetops and launched it in the air. It was early morning. Few
people were about. But here and there a plowman in the field or
a fisherman tending his nets caught sight of them.

"They must be gods!" the simple toilers cried, and they bent
their bodies in reverent worship.

Father and son flew far out over the sea. Daedalus was no
longer worried about Icarus, who managed his wings as easily
as a bird. Already the islands of Delos and Paros were behind
them. Calymne, rich in honey, was on their right hand. But now
Icarus began to yield to the full delight of his new-found powers.
He wanted to soar and swoop. How thrilling it was to rise to a
height, close his wings, and speed down, down, like a thunderbolt, then turn and rise again!

Time after time Icarus tried it, each time daring greater
heights. Then, forgetting his father's warning, he soared higher
still, far up into the cloudless sky.

"Not even the eagle soars as high as this!" the boy thought. "I
am like the gods that keep the wide heaven."

As the words crossed his mind, he felt a warm stream flow
over his shoulders. He had come too close to the blazing sun,
and the sweet-smelling wax that bound the feathers was melt-

ing. With a shock of terror he felt himself hurtling downward. His wings, broken in a thousand parts, were hurtling downward, too. In vain Icarus moved his arms up and down—he could get no hold on the air.

"Father!" he shrieked. "Father! Help! I am falling."

Even as he cried, the deep blue water of the sea—that ever since has been called Icarian—closed over him.

"Icarus! Icarus! Where are you?" Daedalus cried, turning in every direction and searching the air behind, above, and all around. Then his eyes fell on the sea. Tufts of feathers were floating on the crest of the waves.

Too well he understood their meaning. Folding his great wings, he came to earth on the nearest island and fixed his streaming eyes upon the sea. He beat his breast. Wildly he clutched his hair.

"O Icarus, my son!" he wailed. "Even so fell Talus whom my envy slew! The gods have avenged him." He ripped off his glorious wings and stamped upon them. "Cursed be the skill that wrought my son's destruction!" he cried.

Days afterwards, the body of Icarus washed to the shore. There, on the lonely island which bears the boy's name, Daedalus buried his only son.

Orpheus and Eurydice

by Michael Gibson

IF Apollo was the greatest musician of the gods, Orpheus was supreme among the mortals. It was music from Orpheus's lyre which saved all but one of the Argonauts from the temptation of the Sirens. As a result, his fame had spread far and wide over the land of Thrace, where his father was king.

Orpheus was also a poet, whose inspiration came from the nine Muses, and a singer. At court, the people would listen spellbound as he sang the great sagas of his country, plucking the strings of his instrument in soft accompaniment. At times he would wander out into the countryside, playing as he went. The birds and wild beasts that roamed there would draw close to listen and to follow him. Even the trees swayed in time to the tunes he played.

It was while he was strolling alone through the woods that he met the beautiful dryad Eurydice and brought her back to the palace, to be his wife.

The dryads were nymphs of the trees and woods. Sometimes, when she was tired of her busy life at court, Eurydice would visit her former companions. They would sit on a grassy bank while she told them about her strange new city life, where there were hard, paved streets instead of the soft turf of the forest, and stone houses and temples instead of groves of trees. If Orpheus was with her, the nymphs would dance and sing as he played to them.

At other times, Eurydice used to walk by herself through the woods, enjoying the dappled light which came down through the leaves above her and listening to the songs of the birds. She would stoop to pick the pink and mauve cyclamen and wood sorrel which grew beneath the trees and make garlands of their blossoms for her hair. Sometimes she would rest on the bank of a stream and watch butterflies dancing over the water. In the winter months she loved the rustle of the fallen leaves under her feet and would pause to run her hand over the rough bark of her beloved trees.

At times it snowed in that part of Greece. When this happened, Eurydice could see clearly the tracks of rabbits, hares, deer, and the larger beasts which preyed on them. Everything

about her would be white. The familiar woods looked strange yet
somehow even more beautiful. All around was silent; even the
birds would stop singing. If, in the silence, a small gust of wind
sent snow slithering down from the bare branches, Eurydice
would start nervously.

One bright, warm summer's day when the sun was shining,
she was watching a deer feeding in a grassy clearing when suddenly its ears pricked up and it raised its head. For a moment it
stood like this, and then like a shadow it slipped away. A tall
man whom Eurydice had never seen before strode from the trees
into the clearing. He was handsome, but there was a cruel glint
in his eyes which she did not like. He carried a bow and arrows
across his back and stopped when he saw the girl standing there.

"I have heard of the nymphs of the Thracian woods, but you
are the first I have seen," he said. "Everything that people say of
their beauty is true if you are one of them."

Eurydice was not vain and did not like to hear such flattery
from a stranger. "I thank you sir," she said, "but I suggest that
you go on your way, for I have no wish to be disturbed."

"You may be beautiful, but by the gods you have a sharp
tongue!" the man answered. "If you want to be rid of me, tell me
first in which direction the deer I was stalking has gone. You
must have seen it, for it came through here."

Eurydice shook her head. "No, sir," she said. "That I cannot
tell you. It was too pretty to die."

The man frowned. "A nymph you may be but, by thunder,
even the fairest nymphs do not defy a god! Tell me, I say!"

Stubbornly Eurydice shook her head. "A god you may be,"
she said, "though I somehow doubt it, for if you were you would
not behave so rudely. Take care how you speak to me, for my
husband is the king's son and will not take kindly to someone
who does not respect his wife."

The stranger threw back his head and laughed. "The wife of
Orpheus, the poet and singer!" he exclaimed. "I have heard he
loves music more than battle. You threaten me with *him?*
Clearly you do not know who I am."

"No, sir," Eurydice said, more calmly than she felt. "I do not,
and I do not wish to."

"Nevertheless I will tell you," said the stranger. "Perhaps it
will humble your proud spirit a little. I am Aristaeus, the god of
hunters."

"Then you should be more gentle," answered Eurydice, "for
was not your own mother the nymph Cyrene? I have heard the

story of how she was carried off from her home by Apollo and bore his son."

"Gentle? Yes, my mother was gentle. But I learned from my father, the great Apollo, to take what I want when I want it." The stranger paused and then added, gesturing to her: "Come here! I will have a kiss from Orpheus's wife! Then we will see if he dares defy me!" He strode forward, and Eurydice, terrified, turned and fled.

Swiftly she ran through the trees, dodging first right then left. The low boughs brushed her face as she ran and, where the trees grew less thickly, brambles tore at her tunic as if to hold her back. But his life as a hunter had made Aristaeus a fine athlete and he ran as fast as she, crashing through thickets like a wounded boar. Eurydice could hear him behind her. Once she stumbled and thought that she would fall, but she regained her balance and ran on. Her voice echoed through the woods as she cried out desperately for help, but there was no one near to hear. The only answer was a cruel laugh from behind her.

The chase continued through mossy clearings and over half-hidden streams of clear water where the fish swam unconcerned in the shadows under the banks. Eurydice's heart was pounding, but it seemed at last that she was drawing away from her pursuer. As the ground began to rise and the trees became fewer, Aristaeus's footsteps grew more faint.

Presently, she scrambled upwards into the sunlight over a rock-strewn slope. At last the footsteps had ceased. Eurydice could not be sure that she had escaped and she continued upwards until, at the summit of the higher ground, she threw herself down exhausted on a flat-topped rock. Below her and all around she could see the green tops of the trees. From here she would be able to see Aristaeus a long way away, so she decided to rest for a while.

Eurydice saw no more of Aristaeus, and after a while she dozed in the hot sun. The whole world seemed to be at peace and drowsing. Suddenly another sun-lover appeared—a deadly viper which lived on the stony ground surrounding the place where the girl lay. It moved slowly over the warm earth by the flat-topped rock, its forked tongue darting in and out. As it passed near her, Eurydice stirred and turned in her sleep. One of her slender legs now barred the viper's path. The snake hissed and coiled its body quickly, raising its head to strike. Its fangs sank deep, spreading their venom, but Eurydice did not wake. A bee droned lazily by and was gone, and then no more sound was heard. The poison had done its deadly work.

Night came, and still Eurydice had not returned to the palace. At first Orpheus was not seriously worried, for no harm had ever come to his wife on her lonely wanderings in the woods where she was so much at home. But when midnight came, search parties were sent out to scour the surrounding countryside. Their calls echoed through the trees as they searched. Lights flickered here and there through the woods like phantoms. It was morning when they at last found her. Placing her body on a stretcher hastily made from saplings bound with creepers, the searchers carried her back to the palace with heavy hearts.

Orpheus was inconsolable. His father tried to comfort him, but it was no use. Orpheus sat alone, playing sad tunes on his lyre and thinking only of his lost love.

But Aristaeus had been wrong about Orpheus. He was a brave man, braver by far than most, and perhaps his desperation to win back Eurydice gave him a greater courage than he would normally have had. For he decided that he would enter Hades itself and fetch her back to earth from there. Everyone tried to dissuade him. "Not even in your wildest dreams should you consider going there" King Oeagrus told his son. "The dead are the dead and the living the living. You are mad to think you can change the way of the gods. Those who go to the Underworld can never return."

Nevertheless, Orpheus set out, his lyre slung from his shoulder, his mind full only of Eurydice. He journeyed overland to Aornum in Thesprotis, which borders the Ionian Sea. He had heard that a narrow passageway led from here, far beneath the earth, to the river Styx. The river was the only barrier to Hades itself. He found the passage and descended out of the sunlight into the gloom. Water dripped from the dank ceiling and rats scuttled away into the dark corners as he made his way bravely forward. At last the Styx was before him. Charon the ferryman sat there in his boat, waiting for his next cargo of the dead.

Orpheus knew it would not be easy to persuade Charon to take a living cargo but, trusting to the magical powers of his music, he struck a note on his lyre. A rare smile lit the stern face of the boatman. He leaned back in his seat and his eyes closed as the music enveloped him, its wonderful harmonies echoing back from the cavernous walls. Few could have resisted its appeal for long, and Charon succumbed to it completely.

"I can deny nothing to one who can play as you can," he said to Orpheus. "I will take you over the river, though I may pay for it later when my master finds out what I have done." Charon moved to one side to let Orpheus clamber into the boat.

On the other bank stood the guard dog Cerberus, but Orpheus's playing soothed even this fierce animal and Cerberus, like Charon, allowed him to pass.

In due course, Orpheus was brought before Persephone, the queen of the Underworld. Before he spoke he once more played his lyre, and the shades of the dead clustered near to hear his music. Persephone's heart was touched by his story and his music and she agreed to let Eurydice return to earth.

"But on one condition only," she told Orpheus. "She must follow behind you as you go. If you turn round to see her before she reaches the upper air, she must return here for ever."

So Eurydice was brought to them, and the young couple embraced while Persephone looked on with a half-smile, as if she already doubted her decision. But she did not change her mind. The pair crossed the Styx safely and began the long climb up the passage to the surface of the earth. Orpheus never looked back, though he was greatly tempted to make sure that the footsteps he could hear behind him really were those of his beloved wife and not some trickery of the shades. Up and up they climbed, until presently daylight showed ahead of them.

A few minutes later, Orpheus was at the mouth of the cave, and the warmth of the sun was on his face. A great joy flooded through his whole being. What had been only a wild dream of happiness regained had actually come true. He turned to take Eurydice in his arms. However, less strong than he, she had lagged some way behind him in the climb. He saw her dimly coming towards him, still in the shadowy passage. But even as he looked she seemed to fade away and then was gone. He rushed forward but it was too late. She had returned to the shadowy world of the dead and was lost to him forever.

Echo and Narcissus

by E. F. Buckley

THE nymphs, who were hand-maidens of the great goddess Hera, lived on the lower slopes of a mountain near Olympus. When they were not on duty, they sang and played and danced beside the streams and sparkling waterfalls and in the wooded glades. Amongst them all Echo was the gayest and her laugh the merriest, while in story-telling none could touch her. So, when her sisters planned secret fun or mischief, and sometimes even when Zeus sought other company, Echo would be sent to amuse Hera, craftily to hold her attention with some long tale so that the goddess would forget to be jealous and watchful.

The nymph was one of Hera's favorites, and when she looked down at Echo, her stern gaze softened and she would smile and say, "Well, fair nymph, what tale hast thou to tell, or how else wilt thou entertain me today?" And Echo, sitting at Hera's feet, would begin a tale. Sometimes she told a new story, sometimes an old one, embroidering it with her own fancies, and sometimes she would just talk about herself and her doings. Her stories and her chatter were always irresistible and the time would slip away unnoticed, while Hera listened and Echo's companions enjoyed themselves without fear of interruption or of their mistress's anger.

But at last the black day of reckoning came when Hera found out the trick Echo had so often played upon her, and the fire of her wrath flashed forth like lightning.

"The gift with which thou hast deceived me shall be thine no more," she cried. "Henceforward thou shalt be dumb till someone else hath spoken, and then, even if thou wilt, thou shalt not hold thy tongue, but must needs repeat the last words thou hast heard."

"Alas! Alas!" cried the nymphs in chorus.

"Alas! Alas!" cried Echo after them, and could say no more, though she longed to speak to Hera and to beg her forgiveness. And so it was that Echo's voice became useless to her. She could not speak when she would and yet she was compelled to say what others put into her mouth, whether she wished it or no. She left the happy groves where her sisters still played, and retreated, sorrowful and lonely, to the high forest slopes of the mountain.

Now, it chanced one day that a youth, named Narcissus, became separated from his companions in the hunt, and when he
tried to find them he only wandered farther into deep woods on
the mountainside. He was in the bloom of young manhood, and
fair as a flower in spring. But, though his face was smooth, and
soft as any maiden's, his heart was hard as steel. When he was
born, the blind seer Teiresias had made a strange prophecy
concerning him. "So long as he knows not himself, he shall live
and be happy."

Narcissus grew up seeking nothing but his own pleasure; and
because he was so handsome that all who saw him loved him,
he found it easy to get from others what he would. Although he
was loved by many youths and by many maidens he spurned
them all, and himself knew nothing of love, and therefore but
little of grief; for love at the best brings joy and sorrow hand in
hand, and if unreturned, it brings only pain.

When Echo saw Narcissus wandering alone through the
woods, she fell in love with him and followed him wherever he
went, hiding behind the trees and rocks so that he should not
see her. At last, when he found he had really lost his way, he
began to shout for his companions. "Ho, there! Where are you?"
he cried.

"Where are you?" answered Echo.

At the sound of her voice, Narcissus stopped and listened,
but he heard nothing more. Then he called again. "I am here in
the wood—Narcissus."

"In the wood—Narcissus," said she.

"Come hither," he cried.

"Come hither," she answered.

Wondering at the strange voice which answered him, he
looked all about, but could see no one.

"Are you close at hand?" he asked.

"Close at hand," answered Echo.

Wondering the more at seeing no one, he went forward in the
direction of the voice. Echo, when she found he was coming towards her, fled farther, so that when next he called, her voice
sounded far away. But wherever she was, he still followed, and
she saw that she could not escape; for if he called, she had to
answer, and so brought him to her hiding-place. By now they
had come to an opening in the trees, where the green sloped
down to a clear pool in the hollow. Here by the margin of the
water she stood, with her back to the tall, nodding bulrushes,
and as Narcissus came out of the trees she wrung her hands,

and the salt tears dropped from her eyes; for she longed to speak loving words to him, and she could not. When he saw her he stopped.

"Are you she who calls me?" he asked.

"Who calls me?" she answered.

"I have told you, Narcissus," he said.

"Narcissus," she cried, and held out her arms to him.

"Who are you?" he asked.

"Who are you?" said she.

"Have I not told you?" he said impatiently. "Narcissus!"

"Narcissus," she said again, and still held out her hands beseechingly.

"Tell me," he cried, "who are you and why do you call me?"

"You call me?" said she.

Then he grew angry.

"Maiden, whoever you are, you have led me a pretty dance through the woods, and now face to face you only mock me."

"Only mock me," said she.

At this he became yet more angry, and began to abuse her, while she could say nothing of her love, and was forced to echo his cruel words. At last, having had enough of this profitless argument, exhausted by the distance he had covered in his wanderings on the mountain, Narcissus threw himself on the grass by the pool, and would not look at Echo nor speak to her. For a time she stood beside him weeping, and then in misery she left him, and went and hid behind a rock close by. After a while, when his anger had somewhat cooled, Narcissus noticed for the first time the clear pool beside him, and bent over the edge of the bank to drink. As he held out his hand to take the water, there looking up towards him was the fairest face he had ever seen. Narcissus, who had never yet known the pangs of love, at last fell in love, and his heart was set on fire by the face in the pool. With a sigh he held out both arms, and the figure also held out its two arms to him, and Echo from the rock sighed in answer to his sigh. When Narcissus saw the figure stretching out towards him and heard the sigh, he thought that his love was returned, and he bent closer to the water and whispered, "I love you."

"I love you," softly answered Echo from the rock.

At these words he reached down and tried to clasp the figure in his arms. But when he broke the surface of the water the figure vanished. The youth drew back, thinking he had been over-hasty, and waited a while. Then the ripples died away and the face appeared again as clear as before, looking up at him longingly from the water. Once again he bent and tried to clasp the figure, and once again it fled from his embrace. Time after time he tried, and always the same thing happened, and at last he gave up in despair, and sat looking down into the water. Teardrops fell from his eyes, and the face in the pool looked up weeping and in seeming longing and despair. The longer he looked, the more fiercely did the flame of love burn in his breast, till at length Narcissus could bear no more. Determined to reach the desire of his heart or die, he threw himself from the bank into the pool, thinking that in the depths, at any rate, he would find his love. But what he found, among the weeds and stones at the bottom of the pool, was death, and he knew not that it was his own face he had seen reflected in the water below him. Thus were the words of the blind prophet fulfilled: "So long as he knows not himself he shall live and be happy."

Echo, watching from behind the rock, saw all that had happened, and when Narcissus cast himself into the pool she rushed forward, but was too late to stop him. When she found that he had disappeared beneath the surface of the water she sank down on the grass at the edge of the pool and wept and wept. And there she stayed, weeping and sorrowing for her lost love until she wasted away; her body dissolved into air and her bones became stone at the water's edge. But although the nymph herself vanished the power of Hera's curse remained.

To this day, invisible Echo haunts the domed forest clearings, the rocky hillsides, and caves, and vaults, and lofty halls, repeating the words she hears, answering when another calls.

The body of Narcissus was never recovered by his companions, but beside the mountain pool, among the grasses watered by sad Echo's tears, there grew up in the Spring, white and golden flowers which spread—a sweet-scented mass—all round the pool, in memory of the fair youth who had fallen in love with his own beauty.

Perseus

by Alice Low

KING Acrisius of Argos had a beautiful daughter named
Danaë, but he was not satisfied with her, for he wanted a son.
He visited the oracle at Delphi to find out if he would ever have
a male child. To his dismay he was told, "You shall never have a
son. Furthermore, your daughter shall give birth to a son who
shall take your life."

I must make certain that Danaë never has any children, said
the king to himself. And he shut his daughter away from the
world in a bronze house underground, so that no man would
ever fall in love with her and father her child. Nobody could
enter the house, for only a tiny section of the roof was open to
the surface of the earth, to let in light and air.

Poor Danaë! She was all alone, week after week, with just a
patch of sky to look at. Then one day a strange thing occurred.
Suddenly a shower of gold rained down into her house, and
that shower changed into Zeus, who declared his love for her.

Within the year Danaë bore Zeus's son, whom she named
Perseus. Danaë tried to hide Perseus from her father. At last,
though, King Acrisius discovered him and said to Danaë, "One
day this son of yours will kill me. I cannot kill him, for that
would anger his father, Zeus. But I will have the two of you
sealed in a chest and tossed into the sea. If you do not survive,
that will be Poseidon's fault."

"Please, Father, spare us," cried Danaë. "I will keep Perseus by
my side always and make certain that he will never harm you."

But Acrisius said, "The oracle at Delphi never lies, and I
must protect myself."

He ordered carpenters to make a large wooden chest. When it
was finished, he put Danaë and Perseus in it and had it thrown
into the sea.

For a day and a night, Danaë cowered in the chest, holding
Perseus in her arms as the waves tossed them to and fro. Then,
suddenly, Danaë felt a bump, and the chest stopped moving.
"We are on land," she said to Perseus. "But how can we ever get
out of this sealed chest?"

Perseus was too young to understand her, and he cried and
cried because he was hungry. Danaë tried to comfort him, but

his wails continued, which was a good thing. A fisherman, passing by, heard the cries and broke open the chest. His name was Dictys, and he took Danaë and Perseus to his home, where he and his wife cared for them gladly, for they were childless.

Perseus grew into a strong young man and became a fisherman on that small island. He and his mother were content until Dictys's brother, Polydectes, who ruled the island, fell in love with Danaë and tried to force her to marry him. Perseus defended his mother so bravely that Polydectes decided he had to get rid of him.

Pretending he was going to marry another princess, Polydectes asked each guest to bring a wedding gift. Perseus said to Polydectes, "Alas, I am too poor to bring a gift for a ruler and his bride."

And Polydectes said, "Then I shall tell you of a gift you can win for me, but I do not know if you are brave enough to get it."

"Tell me what it is, and I promise I shall get it for you," said Perseus. "I do not lack for bravery."

"Very well," said Polydectes. "I want you to bring me the head of Medusa, the horrible Gorgon."

Perseus was trapped by his bold promise, even though he knew that this feat was impossible for one man alone. Medusa was one of the three Gorgons—huge, hideous winged creatures. Their hair was made of snakes, and their faces were so ugly that anyone who looked at them immediately turned to stone.

Fortunately for Perseus, a goddess and a god overheard that conversation, and not long afterward they appeared to him and offered him their help.

First Athena flew down from Mount Olympus, holding her dazzling shield of brass. She gave it to the astonished Perseus, saying, "You must use this as a mirror when you slay Medusa. In this way you will not look at her directly, but only at her reflection, and so you will not be turned to stone."

Perseus thanked the wise goddess and then said, "But I do not know where Medusa lives. How shall I find her?"

At that moment, Perseus saw a bright light overhead. Hermes, the messenger of the gods, flew down and landed at his side. "I shall be your guide," he said, "and also help you overcome the terrible Medusa. Here is a sword that can never be broken, not even by the hard scales of Medusa's neck."

"This is indeed a wonderful gift," said Perseus. "Now I must be on my way to slay Medusa and bring back her head."

"Not yet," said Hermes. "There are three other things you must have first: winged sandals, a magic wallet, and a cap to make you invisible. These are guarded by the nymphs of the North, and only the Gray Women, who live in a dreary gray land, know where to find *them*. Follow me, and we will begin the long journey."

Hermes guided Perseus to the gray land, where it was always gray twilight. At last they found the shriveled old Gray Women, who had swanlike bodies and human heads, but only one eye among the three of them. Perseus and Hermes hid behind a rock and watched the Gray Women pass the eye around. Each had a turn to put it in the middle of her forehead.

"The next time the eye is passed around," said Hermes to Perseus, "you must grab it and not give it back until they tell you where to find the nymphs of the North."

Perseus waited for the right moment. Then he darted out and snatched the eye. The Gray Women ran around blindly, shouting, "Where is our eye? Who took it?"

"*I* took your eye," Perseus said, "and I will not give it back until you tell me how to find the nymphs of the North."

Of course the Gray Women were anxious to have their eye, and so they immediately gave Perseus detailed directions. He gave them back their eye and went on his way with Hermes.

Once more they traveled far and long, this time over the ocean to the north. The nymphs of the North received them warmly and gave Perseus the three magic gifts.

Perseus put on the cap of invisibility and the magic sandals and, holding the magic wallet, flew after Hermes to the island of the Gorgons. Beneath him he could see stones in the shapes of animals and men, and he shuddered, for he knew that they had once been alive—before they had looked at the fearful Gorgons. But he was confident, now that he was armed with Hermes' sword, Athena's shield, and the three magic gifts.

Perseus hovered over the Gorgons. Fortunately he remembered to look into the mirrorlike shield at their reflections. The three hideous, winged, snake-haired Gorgons were asleep.

But which one is Medusa? he thought. *She is the only one I can kill, for the other two are immortal.* Again Athena came to his aid, saying, "That one in the middle is Medusa. Strike now, while she is asleep."

Perseus flew within inches of Medusa, his sword held ready. Then, looking into the shield, he struck off Medusa's head with one well-aimed blow. He stuffed the head into his magic wallet, which grew large enough to hold the head with all its snakes still hissing and wriggling.

The other two Gorgons woke up when they heard the headless body of Medusa thrashing about. They flew into the air in pursuit of Perseus. But they could not see him, for he had on his cap of invisibility, and he flew away in his winged sandals, faster than the wind.

Now Perseus headed for home alone, for Hermes, his mission accomplished, had left. On his way, Perseus slew a dangerous sea monster that was about to devour a lovely princess named Andromeda. Then Perseus took Andromeda home with him, for she had agreed to be his bride.

As soon as they reached home, Perseus strode into Polydectes' palace and said to the ruler, "I have brought you the head of Medusa."

But Polydectes refused to believe Perseus. "If you even had gone *near* Medusa, you would not be here to tell the tale. What a liar you are!"

Perseus could not stand to be taunted and mistrusted. And now he realized that this cruel ruler had sent him on the chase just to get rid of him. He pulled out Medusa's head to show it to Polydectes, who turned to stone the moment he saw it.

Kind Dictys became ruler of the island, and Perseus sailed to Argos with his mother, Danaë, and his wife, Andromeda. Danaë wanted to see her father, King Acrisius, again and to be reconciled with him. But Acrisius was attending games that were being held in another city.

Since Perseus wanted to take part in the games, he journeyed to that city. There he took his turn at throwing the discus. As the discus left his hand, a sudden wind blew it into the grandstand. It hit King Acrisius, who was a spectator, and killed him. Thus was fulfilled the prophecy of the oracle at Delphi, which had predicted that the king would be killed by his grandson.

Theseus and the Minotaur

retold by Anne Terry White

IN the palace of old King Pittheus of Troezen a grandson was growing up—brave, strong, and handsome. And people said of him: "What wonder that Theseus is so fair and noble? Is not the great god Poseidon his father?"

The young Theseus was pleased enough with being a god's son, the more especially as his cousin Heracles was one. For Theseus idolized the hero whose praises sounded in every court. Often the boy said to himself, "I will be like Heracles and slay wild beasts and giants and evil men." So it was a shock to him to learn that he was no demigod but the son of a mortal—King Aegeus of Athens.

The secret was revealed to him in a curious way. For several years past on his birthday, his mother, the Princess Aethra, had taken him to a great black stone standing by the sea.

"My son," she had always said, "see if you can push this stone aside."

Try as he would, he had never been able to do it. But on his eighteenth birthday he had scarcely exerted his strength when the mighty rock yielded, disclosing a hollow beneath, and in the hollow lay a gold-hilted sword and a pair of embroidered sandals.

"This sword and these sandals were your father's," Theseus' mother said. "Take them up, for now they are yours."

Then she told him about her secret marriage to King Aegeus and how on parting from her he had said: "When my son—if you bear a son—is strong enough to move this stone, give him my sword and my sandals and let him come to Athens and make himself known to me."

Theseus at once put on the sandals and strapped the great gold-hilted sword by his side. He was all on fire to go to Athens.

"I will provide you with a vessel and oarsmen," his grandfather King Pittheus said. "For the roads are beset with robbers."

"Indeed, indeed, grandfather, I will go by land," Theseus protested. "For how can I come to my father with his sword unstained? Greece rings with the fame of Heracles my cousin, and shall I avoid robbers rather than slay them?"

Theseus pleaded so hard that in the end King Pittheus, great as were his fears, gave in and said, "Do according to your spirit."

So Theseus set out on foot and alone.

Now as the young traveler strode lightly along, his mind busy with thoughts of Athens and high deeds, the first of the evildoers who beset the way rushed out at him from the woods. A black bearskin cloaked his bulky body and an iron club was in his hand. He stood squarely in the path, brandishing his weapon and shouting fearful threats.

Theseus did not draw back. "To slay villains like you, have I come this way!" he cried and flung himself boldly on the attacker.

Not in vain had the prince labored to perfect himself in wrestling and boxing. He soon left the savage dead upon the ground. But the iron club he took away and ever after carried with him. Did not Heracles his cousin also bear a club?

Many a time on that journey Theseus was glad of the powerful weapon. For the way to Athens, as his grandfather had warned, was infested with robbers. Three more scoundrels he slew before he reached the river Cephisus not far from Athens. And had not chance put him on his guard, before crossing that river, he might have lost his life. For now there came toward him a villain of another sort, a fellow richly clad and smiling and pleasant of speech.

"Noble traveler," he said to Theseus, "you must come with me and eat and drink of the best my house affords, for it is my custom to show hospitality to all who pass this way."

"I am in haste," Theseus answered, thanking him courteously.

But the other seized hold of Theseus' hands and would not let him go. Theseus did not like to offend one who seemed so hospitable. So against his will he followed the stranger to his house.

Now while they sat at table, his host was called from the chamber, and the slave who poured the wine, whispered to Theseus:

"Young man, flee this house while yet you may! My master is a monster of evil. He will bid you sleep in his famed iron bed which fits all men. Once you are asleep, he will bind you to it. If you are too long for his bed, he will cut off your legs. If you are too short, he will stretch you to fit. Therefore is he called Procrustes, the Stretcher."

Theseus said no word, but grasped his club, which he had laid down by him. And before he left that house, he had fitted Procrustes to his own bed.

News of the hero's exploits traveled fast. Long before Theseus arrived, Aegeus knew that a brave youth from Troezen was on his way to Athens. But the King had no thought that this was his son and anxiously awaited his arrival. For Athens was in turmoil, and the childless King was afraid.

"The people might set him on the throne in my place," he thought.

Now Aegeus' wife was none other than Medea, that same Medea who had taken such fearful revenge on Jason. In her chariot drawn by dragons she had escaped through the air to Athens. There she had gained great influence over the old King and had then got him to marry her. She knew who Theseus was. She, too, feared his coming. But it was for a different reason. "With a hero son by his side, the king will no longer hearken to me as of old," she thought.

And she said to Aegeus: "Let us poison Theseus at the first opportunity. For I have learned by my magic arts that he comes to destroy you."

So when with welcoming cries the Athenians brought the hero to the palace, Aegeus received him graciously, hiding for the moment his evil intentions. Theseus, for his part, was all eagerness. He could hardly wait to make himself known to his father. But the Prince had set his heart on having Aegeus recognize him of his own accord. So he gave no reason for his coming and accepted the King's hospitality merely as any hero might do.

Morning came. Theseus took his place beside Aegeus at the meal that had been set forth. A goblet of wine stood at the youth's place, and Aegeus watched eagerly to see Theseus drain it, for Medea had mixed a deadly poison for him. But Theseus did not even notice the wine. His happy eyes were turned on his father and he waited, a smile on his parted lips, hoping to be recognized. When Aegeus made no sign, the hero quietly laid his sword on the table.

A look of horror spread over Aegeus' face and a loud cry escaped him as he beheld the golden hilt. He reached across the table and dashed the fatal goblet to the floor. Then, weeping, he took his son in his arms and hugged him and passed his hands over the stalwart body and felt the knotting muscles and kissed the fair beardless cheeks of his hero son. Nor could Theseus look enough upon his father.

But Medea knew well that her hour had come, knew well that her witching rule in Athens was over. So once again she summoned her swift-flying dragons. And once more they bore her away—none knew where.

Not long after Aegeus had acknowledged Theseus as his son and heir, Athens was thrown into mourning. Heralds had arrived from Crete to demand for the third time the terrible human tribute which every nine years had to be paid to King Minos.

Years before, Androgeos, the son of Minos, had gone to Athens to take part in the games. He had shown great prowess, overcoming all the Greeks. Provoked by this, Aegeus had treacherously caused Androgeos to be slain, whereupon King Minos made war on him. The King of Crete raised a great fleet and pressed Aegeus so hard that he was glad to make peace at any price. And the price was terrible—a tribute of seven youths and seven maidens to be sent to Crete and thrown to the Minotaur, the monster half-man, half-bull that lived in the Labyrinth.

Theseus saw that the Athenians were deeply angry with his father, who had brought this grief upon them. At once he offered to go to Minos.

"No, no, my son!" Aegeus pleaded. "The victims will be chosen by lot. Wait and see if you are selected. I have but newly found you!"

But Theseus was like a rock. "I will be one of the fourteen," he said, "whether I am chosen or not."

So Aegeus had to yield. Weeping, and with all Athens following, he went with the victims to the dismal ship.

"O my father, do not weep so," Theseus told him. "All is as the gods will. It may indeed be my fate to slay the Minotaur, and we who sail today in sorrow may yet return in joy. If so, you will know the good news from afar. For I promise you, if the Minotaur be slain, the ship that brings us home will not wear these deadly black sails but victorious white ones."

After this the vessel took to the sea, the land slipped away, and the youths and maidens turned their faces toward Crete.

At Cnossos, the capital of Crete, crowds gathered to see the Athenians whom the Minotaur would soon devour. With many a taunt the captives were paraded in front of the palace. Everyone ran out to see the victims, and with them Ariadne, King Minos' lovely daughter. She stood with a throng of her maidens and looked on as did the rest. But her gentle eyes fixed themselves on one alone—on princely Theseus, who, head high and eyes proudly flashing, marched looking neither to the right nor to the left. A surge of sudden love swept over the princess. And as the taunts rose all around her, she promised herself: "He shall not die!"

As soon as night fell, Ariadne stole out of the palace and went secretly to the captives.

"Fair youth," she whispered to Theseus, "I who for my brother's sake should be your enemy am not. Therefore, I have brought you this." And she took from the folds of her dress a glistening sword and put it in Theseus' hand.

He grasped it joyfully and strapped it beneath his garments.

"Now let the Minotaur roar as loud as he will—he will roar in vain!" Theseus said. "Thanks, gracious Princess. May I live to serve you!"

Ariadne then confessed her love, and Theseus, who found it easy enough to give his in return, promised ardently to make her his wife.

"Indeed I would have it so," Ariadne said. "But there is one thing more," she added. "Without it the sword would be useless, for you would never be able to find your way out of the Labyrinth, which the Athenian Daedalus built. The Minotaur's house is a maze. The passages turn and turn and lead into one another and end nowhere. None who enters may come forth again. Take, therefore, this ball of thread. Tie one end to the inside of the door and unwind the ball as you go. Then, winding it again, you will be able to retrace your steps."

So it was that the hero met the Minotaur in the gloomy depths of the Labyrinth and was not afraid. He came upon the monster sleeping and leaped on him and battled furiously with him. And when the creature lay dead at his feet, Theseus picked up the ball of thread and wound it back to the entrance.

What joy there was when Theseus' glad voice resounded through the passages and his companions saw their leader emerge! What embracing, what happy talk of home! With stealthy steps they made their way to their vessel, where Ariadne stood anxiously waiting for them. Deftly they hoisted sail, dipped their oars, and left the harbor so noiselessly that the Cretans never awoke to realize their loss.

Meantime at Athens King Aegeus daily mounted the cliffs by the sea and sorrowfully strained his old eyes in the direction of Crete. At last he saw the ship approaching—and his heart died within him. Black sails drank the wind. In the joy of homecoming, Theseus had forgotten to change the dismal sails of mourning.

"My son is dead!" the unhappy King cried out. "Why, then, do I live?"

Grief overpowered him and he cast himself headlong into the sea, which ever after has borne his name.

The Judgment of Paris

by Max J. Herzberg

ONE of the most beautiful of the Nereids was the silvery-footed Thetis, who dwelt with her sisters in the depths of the sea, but was a favorite of Juno* and often visited the heights of Olympus. So lovely was she that both Jupiter and Neptune wished to marry her, but the oracles declared that her son would be greater than his father, and neither of the deities dared risk being overthrown. She was therefore given in marriage to a mortal, Peleus, king of the Myrmidons of Thessaly.

To the marriage feast of Peleus and Thetis came all the gods, who brought many rich gifts. But one deity had not been invited to the celebrations—*Eris,* or *Ate,* the goddess of discord. She was greatly enraged at the oversight, and resolved that she would take revenge. While the merrymaking was at its height, therefore, she suddenly appeared in the midst of the revelers and threw upon the ground a wonderful apple, brought from the Garden of the Hesperides, and labeled "For the Fairest."

Immediately a contention arose as to who should have the apple. All the contestants finally withdrew, except three: Juno, Venus, and Minerva. They appealed to Jupiter to settle the dispute and award the apple, but he wisely declined to do so. He agreed, nevertheless, to appoint an arbitrator, and told the three goddesses that Paris of Troy would make the decision.

So the three goddesses then hastened to Paris. Troy was a city in Asia Minor; it was sometimes called Ilion or Ilium. Priam reigned over Troy. He had been twice married, the second time to Hecuba, and had fifty sons, two of whom were of particular note: Hector, one of the noblest heroes of ancient times, and Paris, who was destined to cause the destruction of his people. At the birth of Paris it had been prophesied that he would bring disaster to Troy, and he had consequently been exposed on a mountainside. But some shepherds had found him and had brought him up, and he was at this time a very handsome and attractive youth.

*Juno: Roman name for the Greek goddess Hera, queen of the gods (See page 3 for a table of Greek gods and their Roman equivalents.)

The three goddesses came to him as he tended his sheep. They told him that he must decide which of them was the fairest and to which of them should go the Golden Apple. Each whispered secretly how she would reward him if he gave her the apple. Juno promised him great power and happiness in his domestic life. Minerva assured him of wisdom and of respect from everyone. But Venus promised him the most beautiful woman in the world for his wife, and Paris handed the Golden Apple to Venus. He gained her favor, but won for himself and the Trojans the undying hatred of Juno and Minerva.

There was no doubt as to who was the most beautiful woman then living. She was Helen, daughter of Leda and Jupiter (who had appeared to Leda in the form of a swan), and sister of the great athletes, Castor and Pollux. Even as a child she had inspired almost awe-struck admiration because of her surpassing loveliness. When she passed into girlhood the foremost chieftains of Greece sought her in marriage, and for a time it seemed as if the rivalry for her hand would bring about a deadly war. Among these chieftains, however, there was one very wise man, Ulysses (Greek: Odysseus).

Ulysses proposed that all the suitors of Helen take a solemn oath, not only pledging themselves to abide peacefully by whatever decision she made, but also agreeing that if ever anyone attempted to molest either Helen or her husband, all the others would help him and punish the aggressor. All the chieftains agreed to this oath, and thereupon Helen chose as her husband Menelaus, king of Sparta, whose brother was Agamemnon, king of Mycenæ and the most powerful ruler in Greece.

For a time matters rested as they were. Then Paris reminded Venus of her promise, and she urged him to go to Greece and visit Sparta. There, with the help of the goddess, Paris induced Helen to elope with him, and the pair returned hastily to Troy. Before this Priam had acknowledged Paris as his son; and now when he returned with Helen, he received them in his home, but reluctantly, for he guessed what troubles were in store for him and his people.

The Trojan War

by Ingri d'Aulaire and Edgar Parin d'Aulaire

HELEN had been the Queen of Sparta for many happy years, and her fame as the most beautiful woman on earth had spread all over, when Aphrodite promised her to Paris. The Trojans begged Paris to forget Aphrodite's promise, or a terrible misfortune would surely befall them. But Paris ignored their warnings and sailed across the Aegean Sea, to steal Helen from King Menelaus and bring her back to Troy.

Helen sat serene and happy, surrounded by her ladies, weaving and sewing her finest wools, when Paris entered the palace in Sparta. Just as she looked up and saw him, Eros shot an arrow of love into her heart. She gathered her treasures without hesitation and eloped with him for Troy.

A brisk wind carried them out to sea, but before they had sailed far, the wine-dark waters grew glassy and calm, and Nereus, the kind old man of the sea, rose from the depths. He warned them to return or dire woe would befall them and their kin. But Helen and Paris had eyes and ears only for each other and did not hear his warning.

They landed in Troy and the Trojans received her with great joy, proud that the most beautiful woman on earth was now Helen of Troy.

But Menelaus was not a man to stand idly by, whether or not his queen had been promised to Paris by a goddess. He reminded Helen's old suitors of their oath. They joined him with all their warriors, and it was not long before a huge Greek fleet arrived in Troy to fetch Helen back to Sparta. The Trojans refused to give Helen up, and Troy was hard to conquer, for it was surrounded by a high wall built by Apollo and Poseidon. After long talks, it was decided that Paris and Menelaus should fight in single combat and Helen would go to the winner. Paris was no warrior. He preferred to rest on silken pillows and gaze into Helen's beautiful eyes. But Aphrodite came to his rescue and hid him in a cloud and since Menelaus could not find his opponent, the duel was undecided. Then the two armies clashed together.

For ten long years, the Greeks and the Trojans fought over Helen. The gods watched with great interest and even took part in the fighting themselves. Hera, angry with Paris for not giving the apple to her, fought for the Greeks. Wise and just Athena was also annoyed with Paris, so even though she was protectress of Troy, she fought for the Greeks. Ares fought wherever the battle was hottest, and when he himself was wounded, he frightened both armies with his howls. Sweet Aphrodite herself entered the raging battle to help her darling Paris and she also was wounded. "Enough!" called Zeus, and he ordered all the gods to withdraw from the battle. They sat on the walls of Troy and watched the mortals decide the outcome for themselves.

Many great heroes fell on both sides, but the Greeks could not storm the mighty walls of Troy and the Trojans could not put the Greeks to flight as long as Achilles, the invulnerable son of Thetis, fought for them. Though Paris was no great marksman, fate had chosen him to slay the great hero Achilles. Apollo, unseen by the other gods, ran to Paris's side and guided his hand as he drew taut his bow. The arrow struck Achilles in the heel, his only vulnerable spot. Mortally wounded, he fell to the ground. The Greeks mourned greatly the loss of their hero Achilles, and took their revenge on Paris. He fell, pierced by one of the poisoned arrows that Heracles had given to Philoctetes.

Shortly afterward, the Greeks broke camp, boarded their ships, and sailed away. They left on the shore a large wooden horse. The Trojans thought they had finally routed the Greeks, and in triumph, they pulled the horse into their city as a trophy. But the horse was hollow and filled with Greek warriors. In the dark of the night, they crept out and opened wide the city gates. The wily Greeks had not left, but had been hiding behind an island. Now they came pouring into the city and proud Troy was destroyed.

Helen was brought back to Sparta in triumph to sit among her ladies as lovely as ever, embroidering in lavender and purple threads on the finest wools.

Of the royal house of Troy no one but Aphrodite's son Aeneas, his father, and his young son remained. The goddess returned to take them out of the smoking ruins and lead them to safety.

The Wanderings of Odysseus

by Michael Gibson

AFTER Troy had fallen, the Greek armies did not all sail back to Greece together. Once their common purpose was achieved, some of the commanders separated from the rest and went their own way. The journey from Troy to Greece does not look a long one on a map, but it was a journey full of dangers, especially when gods and monsters played a part. Odysseus, whose plan had brought about the fall of Troy, took many weary years to reach his home in Ithaca.

Odysseus and his ships sailed first of all to a part of Thrace called Circones, which lay to the west of two great rivers, the Hebrus and the Ergines. Here, their landing was opposed by the inhabitants of the district and the Greeks were forced to take to their ships without loading up the supplies and water they had hoped to find. They had intended to follow the Thracian coastline on their homeward journey. In this way they would always be near to land and could run for shelter if necessary. But it was the season of rough weather. Gales blew them out to sea and for many days they ran before winds of almost hurricane force, fearing for the safety of their ships.

Odysseus's ship was separated from the rest of the fleet and soon he and his crew had little idea of where they were. At last the winds eased, the seas went down, and land was sighted. It was the coast of Libya, the country of the Lotus-eaters and Odysseus made a landing there to replenish his supplies of drinking water. Although they had been warned against it, some of his soldiers tasted the seed of the lotus, a magical bean which so confused the minds of those who ate it that they remembered nothing of their former lives. These men wandered off, not knowing where they had come from, caring for nothing but dreams, and Odysseus, afraid that others might be tempted, called the rest of his soldiers back to the ships and weighed anchor without delay.

Their next call was at the island of Sicily, home of the Cyclopes. These were giant men, wild and unkempt, who lived on human flesh. Each had one eye only, gleaming balefully from the middle of his forehead. The terrible Polyphemus, taller even than all the rest, was their leader. He was a son of Poseidon and a nymph, and in his early days he and his followers had lead a more peaceful life. They had worked in the island forge doing fine metalwork and making thunderbolts for Zeus, guided by the watchful smith god Hephaestus. But under the evil influence of Polyphemus they had abandoned their trade and now lived by preying on the towns and villages of the countryside, stealing corn and herds and frightening the people.

All of this was unknown to Odysseus, and when he and his men had landed they set out to explore. They climbed the steep hillside above the bay where they had anchored, making their way between the rocks and boulders that dotted the slope. Ahead of them was a low cliff and as they drew near to it they could see the opening of a cave. In front of it, some long-eared goats were grazing.

"Wait here," Odysseus told his men, "and keep out of sight."

The men took cover behind the rocks while their leader went on alone, moving with great caution. Close to the cave he paused and listened, but there was no sound except the sighing of the wind across the bleak hillside. He was reassured, but nonetheless he drew his sword as he crossed the last few meters to the cave entrance and looked inside. At first it was too dark to make out anything, but as his eyes became accustomed to the gloom he could see that the place was empty. It was much larger than he had imagined from outside, but there was no sign that it was occupied. There was only a pile of bones in one corner, indicating that it had been, or possibly still was, the lair of a wild animal of some kind. If so, the animal was not there now. Odysseus and his men would give it a rough welcome if and when it returned.

Odysseus went out into the afternoon sunshine and called to his men. "We will make this our camp until we can find a better one," he said. "Tomorrow we will look for a town or village and buy grain and oil and other provisions. For today, we could do worse than feast on goats' meat."

The men set to work killing some of the goats and roasting them over a fire which they lit in the cave. They squatted in a circle round the fire as they ate hungrily: fresh meat was something they had not seen for many weeks. Evening was drawing in by the time they had finished and the light in the cave was fading fast. Then, with dramatic suddenness, it vanished completely. Foolishly they had posted no sentries and they had heard no sound. Now when they looked round to see why it had gone so dark, they saw the gigantic figure of Polyphemus blocking the cave entrance completely, his single eye glowing red in the light from their fire. He was a terrifying sight; even Odysseus was afraid, though he put on a brave show.

"Can it be, stranger, that we have inadvertently made ourselves free with your flocks and your home?" he asked. "If so, you must pardon us, for we are strangers and it seemed the place was deserted."

But the giant only grunted in reply. Then he turned and went outside once more. Odysseus sprang to his feet.

"Quickly!" he said. "Before he comes back we must get . . .". But he had no time to finish his sentence, for the cave mouth had darkened once again as Polyphemus came back, driving his flock of goats in front of him. Once inside, he pulled a gigantic boulder across the cave mouth so that it was closed completely. Then, ignoring Odysseus and his companions, he lay down on the floor. Soon his snores echoed through the cave like thunder.

As it seemed unlikely that any sound they made would wake him, the men began to talk together, though they kept their voices low. "I have heard of giants such as these," Odysseus said. "It would seem that we are among the Cyclopes, which is not the happiest place to be."

"Do they not feed on human flesh?" one of the sailors asked.

Odysseus nodded. "So they say. But they may go several days between their feasting," he told them. "Just the same, only luck has saved us from being roasted on this fire. We must escape as quickly as possible, for who knows what tomorrow may bring?"

They crept quietly to the cave entrance, but try as they might, the gigantic boulder which blocked the opening could not be moved. Eventually they had to give up. They dared not attack the giant while he slept, for even if they did succeed in killing him, they would still be trapped.

An uneasy night passed. In the morning Polyphemus drove the goats from the cave and pulled the rock across the opening from outside. They saw no more of him that day. The imprisoned men passed each hour in dread. Another night must inevitably come and with it, who knew what horrors?

But while some of the men gave themselves up to despair, Odysseus was busy plotting and planning. After a while he thought of a possible way in which they could escape. He took a shaft of wood and after sharpening one end, hardened it in the embers of the fire. Then he hid it under a goat skin on the floor and settled down to wait with the others.

That night Polyphemus came back and behaved just as he had

done before. He brought in the flock of goats, moved the great slab of rock across the entrance, and settled down to sleep. Perhaps he had already fed or perhaps the band of Greeks were just lucky to have been in the cave during a period of fast, but soon his snores rumbled through the cavern once more.

When he judged that the night was nearly gone, Odysseus crept quietly to where the wooden shaft was hidden. Taking it out from under the skin, he heated the point in the fire until its sharpened end glowed red. Before it had time to cool he had crossed the cave to the sleeping figure and plunged the glowing stake into Polyphemus's single eye.

With a great roar of rage and pain the blinded giant staggered to his feet. Helplessly he blundered about the cave, arms outstretched, trying vainly to find his attackers, as they dodged away, always managing to keep behind him. At length he gave up and felt his way towards the entrance to the cave. Once there, he groped for the boulder and pushed it aside, but he did not venture out. Instead he crouched waiting by the opening, his huge, hairy fingers curled like talons. Obviously he knew the men would try to escape as soon as they could, and he was ready to seize them as they tried to pass him.

Odysseus had briefed his men well. Already each had captured a goat and now, clasping the long hair of the goats" sides, they hung underneath them as the frightened animals made for the open doorway. Hearing the skuffle of their hooves on the stone floor, Polyphemus began to feel about, but all his hands touched was the familiar hair of the goats' backs and he suspected nothing. One by one the goats trotted past him out into the open air, and with them went the men, to freedom.

They lost no time in scrambling down the hill to their ship. As they rowed clear of the shore and hoisted their sail, Odysseus, standing in the stern, raised his voice and cried:

"Farewell, blind giant! Know that it was not the gods who took your sight, but mere weak men whom you could have destroyed with one finger!"

At the sound, Polyphemus came out from the cave, the huge boulder with which it had been closed held high above his head.

"Farewell!" Odysseus called yet again. The giant turned to the direction of the sound and hurled the boulder with all his strength after the fleeing ship. Then he stumbled to his knees. The boulder fell short, but not much more than a boat's length from the ship's stern. The vessel rocked dangerously, but it soon recovered itself. The crew looked back to see Polyphemus, a lonely, helpless figure, kneeling on the hillside.

With the help of Aeolus, king of the winds, Odysseus sailed to within sight of his island home on Ithaca. Aeolus had tied up all the adverse winds in a goatskin, but thinking that it contained treasure, the sailors opened it up while their captain slept. Thus they were blown away from the shore again and swept far to the west. At length they reached Aeaea, an island ruled by the goddess Circe. She had a reputation for disliking mankind and Odysseus sent a group of about twenty men to spy out the land before attempting to find food or water.

A man by the name of Eurylochus was chosen to lead the party. At first the goddess seemed friendly enough. But there was a look in her eye that Eurylochus did not care for and, when she invited the visitors to a feast, he sent the others but waited outside himself, watching. It was as well that he did so, for no sooner had the men sat down than Circe cast a spell over them which turned them into pigs.

Eurylochus made his way stealthily back to the ship and told his leader what had happened. Faced with an enchantress such as Circe, it was difficult even for Odysseus to know what to do. He was about to set out to attempt a rescue, armed only with his sword, when Hermes appeared. The god told him that he could be protected against Circe's spells by the white flower of a magic herb called moly which grew on the island. Armed with blooms of this herb Odysseus faced the goddess, and when her spell failed to work on him he threatened her. She begged for mercy.

"Only if you release my men will I spare you," he told her. Instantly the pigs became men once more. Nevertheless, Circe was reluctant to let the party go, for she had fallen in love with Odysseus and wanted him to become her consort. He stayed on for a while, anxious though he was to be on his way, for he suspected that she might well have other powers to harm them. He avoided angering her, but left her in little doubt that he did not wish to stay forever. Eventually she promised that he and his men would be released if they went first to the Underworld. There he was to consult the seer Teiresias, who would tell him what the future held. If he said that Aeaea should be their home they must abide by this, but Odysseus must return in any case to tell the goddess what the answer had been.

In the Underworld, Odysseus rejoiced at meeting many of his old comrades, but the news from Teiresias was not encouraging.

Though he would eventually reach Ithaca in safety, he would find that in his absence others had seized his lands and property. Even now they were fighting among themselves about who should have the largest share of the spoils.

Their mission to the Underworld completed, Odysseus and his men sailed back to Aeaea as they had promised. Fortunately, Circe kept her part of the bargain and did not oppose their departure. She even warned them of some of the perils they might encounter on their voyage and told them how these might be overcome.

First they had to pass the rocky coast where the Sirens lived. These creatures used to lure sailors from their ships with their singing. Their voices were so beautiful and their songs so haunting that anyone who heard them plunged to their deaths in the waves to remain near them. Following Circe's advice, Odysseus ordered his men to stop their ears with wax so that they could not hear the singing. He himself had heard so much about their music that he was determined to listen, but he made his men lash him fast to the mast, so that he could not escape. Even if he pleaded with them for his freedom as they sailed by, they were to take no notice.

In this way Odysseus and his men sailed past the Sirens and Odysseus became one of the few men to hear the Sirens' song and live. "Though at the time," he later said, "I would gladly have sacrificed my life for the sound of their voices."

Ahead lay further dangers. They had to pass through a narrow channel between towering rocks where the monsters Scylla and Charybdis lay in wait, like the Sirens, to trap passing ships. As the ship went by, Scylla, a six-headed monster, reached out her long arms and, uttering a curious yelping sound, clawed six sailors from the deck and devoured them. Odysseus altered course quickly, but in doing so steered perilously close to the great whirlpool of Charybdis.

Several times a day Charybdis would suck huge quantities of water into her enormous mouth and then spew it out again, so that the channel between the rocks seethed and whirled, drawing down into the depths even the mightiest ships which came within range. However, the wind was strong and the men pulled for their lives with the oars; they felt their stern dragged round and for several long minutes it seemed that they, too, would be sucked down. Somehow, however, they passed safely through.

Saddened by the loss of their six comrades, they rowed on. As they passed Sicily once more they found that their drinking water was again running low. They turned in towards the island and anchored in a cove well away from the place where the Cyclopes lived. They were now in the part of the island ruled by the god Helios. Odysseus warned his men to behave peaceably, and not to take anything. They had, he said, had troubles enough. However, the sailors had already seen cattle grazing nearby and the prospect of eating fresh meat was a temptation they could not resist. While their leader was sleeping, they killed and roasted some cattle from Helios's herds. The god was outraged and, complained to Poseidon. He in turn had not forgiven Odysseus for blinding his son Polyphemus and when the ship sailed again he called up a wild storm. The ship foundered and everyone but Odysseus himself was drowned.

It was only because he was a strong swimmer that Odysseus was able to save himself. He managed to lash together fragments of wreck into a raft, but for many days he drifted helplessly before the gale, cold, hungry and with no fresh water to drink. The storm carried his raft back to the perilous channel where Scylla and Charybdis waited and this time his frail craft was sucked deep into the whirlpool. Odysseus struggled desperately to save himself, the rush of the waters filled his ears and spray almost blinded him. Death was very close. Then, as his raft was tossed up again in the centre of the whirling water, he stood upright and managed to grab at a fig tree which grew out of the cliff side. He pulled himself up onto this just as the raft vanished from sight. Then the gaping mouth of Charybdis closed, and the rushing waters became calm. Odysseus saw his chance and, dropping quickly from the tree, he swam to safety, out of the whirlpool's reach.

However, it was only a comparative safety for he was now far from any friendly shore; exhaustion could easily have proved more deadly than the twin monsters. Fortunately, the white goddess Leucothea came to him disguised as a seabird. In her beak she carried a veil which she told Odysseus to wind about his waist. Wearing this, he would never drown.

His journey was now nearly done. Helped by the veil, he was carried to the shores of an island, where he was found by Nausicaa, daughter of King Alcinous. He told her the story of his adventures, and the king gave him passage on a ship which was bound for his own island of Ithaca. When he reached it, he was sleeping. The sailors did not like to disturb his rest, so they carried him gently to the beach and left him there.

But though he was home at last after so many years, there were still troubles in store. Presently he woke up to find the goddess Athene beside him. "The seer Teiresias predicted that you would return unharmed," she said. "That much has been achieved satisfactorily. But remember that he also said other things."

"That my possessions would be in the hands of others. Is that what you mean?" Odysseus asked. "There should be little difficulty in dealing with them once I reveal myself. But what has happened to my wife Penelope? How has she survived in all this? And my son Telemachus?"

"Telemachus has gone to Sparta to try to gain some news of you from Menelaus and Helen, who recently returned from Troy," Athene said. "He has been powerless to stop what has been happening, for your enemies have been many and powerful, and indeed they are at this moment plotting to kill Telemachus on his return. In this way they hope to destroy the last protector of Penelope. She has waited faithfully for you. Many men have tried to persuade her into marriage, but with her son's help she has refused them all. They are all persistent and some have threatened violence, but she has held them off by promising that she will accept one or other of them when the tapestry she is weaving is complete. Each day she works at it and each night she unravels what she has done. But such a stratagem cannot succeed forever, particularly if Telemachus is taken from her."

As he listened, Odysseus's anger grew. "This must stop at once!" he cried. "I do not fear these suitors, even if there are a hundred of them!" He drew his sword purposefully.

But Athene advised caution. Even if he did succeed in killing all the men who were against him, he perhaps did not realize how the long years away had changed him. Could he be certain that his wife would not turn away from him, thinking that he was simply another stranger seeking her hand and fortune?

Odysseus listened to what the goddess said and knew that she was right. A few more days' delay would make little difference. Athene suggested a plan. First, he let her turn him by magic into a tattered, bent old man, with white hair and a shambling gait. Then the goddess took him to the hut of Eumaeus, a shepherd who had worked for Odysseus before the war. She also sent Telemachus hurrying back from Sparta to join him there, guiding him around the trap which had been set for him by Penelope's suitors. Athene allowed Odysseus to return briefly to his true form, and the two men were let into the secret. But Telemachus, seeing a much older man than he remembered, had doubts, which proved how wise the goddess's caution had been.

"All Ithaca is certain that my father must have perished," said Telemachus. "I would gladly believe that this is not so, but how can I be sure that this is not one more plot to bring about the complete downfall of our family?"

At that moment they heard a sound from the door and, looking round, saw an old staghound with a grizzled muzzle come slowly through it. Many was the time in his younger days that he had hunted with Odysseus. At the sight of his master, the old dog's ears pricked up and his legs seemed to take on an extra spring. He came straight to Odysseus with his tail wagging and rubbed affectionately against him. Telemachus had no further doubts, but Athene advised that for the moment the news should be kept from Penelope. She might not be able to hide her joy from the people who crowded round her all the time and it would be best if she continued to behave exactly as before.

Back in the disguise of an old man, Odysseus went with Eumaeus and Telemachus to the palace to look around and see things for himself. There, the usurping nobles were eating and drinking and making free use of all Odysseus's possessions. When Odysseus appeared they laughed at him and made him the butt of their jokes, showing no sign of the respect that was due to an old man. Penelope, sad-faced and resigned, sat among them, and Odysseus knew that for her sake he must be patient and take their insults without reply.

The nobles were so sure of their power that they no longer kept their weapons with them as they feasted. The swords and spears were stored in an anteroom and the first thing Odysseus did was to instruct Eumaeus to remove them and hide them in the bushes in the garden. The nobles noticed nothing, and the feasting continued as one suitor after another tried to persuade Penelope to marry him. At first she was as firm as before, but perhaps even she was growing weary of the never-ending struggle. There seemed to be signs that she was beginning to waver and, seeing this, Telemachus spoke.

"If any of you men seek to supplant my father Odysseus, you must prove that you are at least as skilled as he with the bow," he said to the assembled company. Perhaps Penelope heard something in her son's voice which gave her hope, or perhaps she simply knew that he must have a good reason for speaking like this.

"A reasonable condition, and I agree," she said. "He that can shoot an arrow with Odysseus's bow through no fewer than twelve axe-rings shall have my hand."

The next morning the contest began and one by one the suitors tried to string and draw the bow. It was, however, so stout that they could not even bend it and their faces reddened with exertion and shame. Each new man was determined to show up those who had gone before, but at length all of them had tried without success. The last man threw the bow from him in disgust and anger.

As he did so, there was a stir from the back of the watching crowd and it parted as the white-haired old man they had mocked so pitilessly hobbled through. They jeered at him again as he picked up the bow, but the jeering soon turned to a murmur of wonder as the old man bent it easily. Stringing an arrow, he let it fly straight through the twelve axe-rings which had been placed upright in the ground.

For a long moment there was silence. Then the old man straightened and suddenly Odysseus was standing there. No one doubted now that this was the king. As one man, the suitors turned and rushed to the anteroom. By the time they had discovered that their weapons had vanished, Odysseus and Telemachus were attacking them, their swords whirling around their heads. Many fell mortally wounded; the rest ran away.

Odysseus was home.

The Wanderings of Aeneas

by Dr. William Montgomerie

GREEK soldiers, from the Wooden Horse and from the hidden Greek ships, had surprised the Trojans and were burning Troy, house by house. Priam, the king, was dead, dragged from the altar of Zeus, and murdered in front of his wife. Many of the Trojan heroes, in a last effort to save their city, perished in a combat they knew to be hopeless. Aeneas was fighting among them, but when Priam was killed his thoughts turned to his own wife and child and his old father. Suddenly his mother, the goddess Aphrodite, appeared before him. It was his duty, she said, to escape with his family to another country. She led him through the fire and slaughter safely to his own house.

At first Aeneas' father, who was old and very lame, felt he had lived his life and refused to leave Troy. But when the hair on the head of his little grandson seemed to burst into flame, and he saw a shooting star fall among the trees of Mount Ida, Anchises accepted these wonders as a sign from the gods, and agreed to leave. Aeneas, taking his father on his back and holding his son by the hand, led his wife and servants, carrying the images of the family gods and other treasures, out of the house. Keeping to the shadows, by lanes and by-ways they at last made their escape through the city gates. Then Aeneas discovered his wife was not with them. Fearing she had become lost in the crowds he went back to look for her. When her ghost appeared, he realized she had been killed, and was lost to him forever; but her spirit spoke, consoling him. She told him not to grieve but to escape to fulfill his destiny. "Your fate, my dear husband," she said, "is to cross the sea to Italy, where, by the river Tiber, you will found a new kingdom and take a new wife to be your queen."

Aeneas, his household, and other refugees from Troy spent the winter months camping on the wooded slopes of Mount Ida. They cut down trees and built as many ships as were needed for all the company. When the little fleet of twenty ships was ready they set course for the north-west in search of the new land.

First they put in at a harbor in Thrace, but finding that the king of that country had murdered a former companion of Aeneas, they sailed south to the little island of Delos, where Apollo and Artemis had been born. In the temple of Apollo, the voice of the oracle spoke to them in these words:

"Go and look for your ancient mother!"

Temple prophecies were often puzzling, and the voyagers tried to guess what the oracle could mean. Anchises said that their "ancient mother" must be Crete, the island of their ancestors, where there was another Mount Ida. So the ships sailed still farther south, to Crete. Here they began to lay the foundations of their city but their work was not blessed: a plague broke out, crops withered, animals sickened and died. In this desperate state Anchises urged Aeneas to go to the nearest temple of Apollo for advice. But that night the images of the gods they had brought from Troy appeared beside his bed and spoke to Aeneas, giving him a message from Apollo. They were wrong in thinking Crete their destined home. They must leave it and sail to Italy, where the Trojan race had come from long ago.

So far the voyagers had been sailing among the beautiful Aegean islands, but now they turned west, round the south of Greece, into the Ionian Sea. A storm which lasted three days drove the ships off course and on to the shore of an unknown island. While the exhausted Trojans were eating the roasted flesh of ox and goat, taken from herds browsing in the flat fields, terrible, evil-smelling, monstrous birds with girls' faces and long talons, swooped over them and carried off the food. They did this again and again and could not be driven away. The weary travellers could neither eat nor rest. These creatures, the Harpies, took their food, and the stench from their bodies was overwhelming. Unwittingly Aeneas and his companions had landed on one of the Strophades. These islands belonged to the Harpies and so did the animals the Trojans had slain for food. Celano, who led the Harpies, screamed from a rock the prophecy that before their journey was over and they built their new city the voyagers would be so tormented by hunger that they would even eat the platters their food had been on. Aeneas and his companions lost no time in taking to the ships and leaving that vile place.

*

At one point in the journey, the god Apollo, through Helenus of Troy, gave a message to Aeneas. Apollo predicted that on his way to Italy, Aeneas would endure Much, but he would know he was at his journey's end by the presence of a sow with thirty piglets. Apollo also counseled Aeneas that when he landed on Italy's western coast, he should confer with the Sybil, who would tell him his future. He urged Aeneas to pay special homage to Hera, who was still bitter that Aeneas's mother, Aphrodite, had been given the "Apple of the Fairest" by Paris of Troy.

During Aeneas's travels, Hera managed to cause trouble by convincing Aeolus, god of the winds, to free rough winds and create a terrible storm. The storm was doused by Poseidon. Upset by the turn of events, Aphrodite implored Zeus to stop Hera's interference. He reassured her that Aeneas would live to fulfill his destiny—to go to Italy and establish a new civilization.

As Aeneas neared Italy, hera again made her presence known, as she disguised herself and encouraged the Trojan womenfolk to burn Aeneas's ships. Zeus stopped the fire, but Aphrodite begged for help to ensure her son's safe journey. The god Poseidon, asking first for the sacrifice of one crew member, protected the ship until it reached Cumae.

A white marble temple to Apollo stood high on the cliff. Beside the temple a cavern had been deeply cut in the rock and from here the famous Sybil shouted her oracles, which came up in a hundred voices, echoing through the hundred passages which led from her underground cave. The Sybil told Aeneas to pray to Apollo for a true prophecy. Then suddenly she began to rave in frenzy as the power of the god possessed her and spoke from her mouth:

O gallant Aeneas, at last after many perils you have come safe to Cumae; so too shall you come safe to Latium but there trouble awaits you and a terrible war. The river Tiber will flow red with blood. Nor will Hera cease to persecute you. As Helen brought calamity to Troy, so here too marriage with a foreign bride will be a source of affliction. But be resolute. A happy turn in your fortunes comes when you least expect it with help from a Greek city.

Then the Sybil was silent and her frenzy ceased.

Aeneas said that the prospect of further trials did not daunt him, but that he had a favor to ask. "May I visit the shade of my dear father in the Lower World of the Dead? If Orpheus could safely make the journey and return, and Polydeuces and Theseus and Heracles too, may not I, the son of golden Aphrodite, be conducted thither?"

"Easy is the descent to the Underworld," answered the Sybil. "The difficulty is to return again to the sweet upper air. But there is a way there from nearby Lake Avernus, and in the dark woods surrounding the lake grows a certain tree which has among its branches one single golden bough. If you, Aeneas, can pluck this golden bough Fate is with you, and you may safely make the journey and return."

Two of Aphrodite's doves led Aeneas to the tree by the lake, and perched beside the golden bough. Aeneas broke off the bough—which we call mistletoe—and brought it back to the Sybil.

First, sacrifices were made to the rulers of the Country of the Dead, and then Aeneas followed the Sybil below the ground. Looking about him as they went along the path which led to the Lower World, Aeneas saw many of the horrific creatures of legend—Hydra, the monster slain by Heracles; the Chimaera, which had the head of a lion, the hinder parts of a dragon, the body of a huge goat with scales and bristles, and a fiery breath; and the Gorgons, one of whom—Medusa—had snakes on her head, fangs for teeth, and eyes that turned men to stone; and the dreadful hundred-handed giant, Briareus.

When they came to the river Styx, over which Charon ferries the dead, Aeneas was sorely troubled to see a miserable crowd of spirits on the marshy bank, who jostled and surged forward trying to get on to the ferry. Every time they came near Charon pushed them back with his oar. "Who are they?" Aeneas asked. "They are those who came here straight from death," said the Sybil sadly. "Without proper funeral rites they may not cross, and are doomed for at least a hundred years to wait here, aimless and desolate."

The Sybil then showed Charon the golden bough and unwillingly he took the living Aeneas and the Sybil across. They threw drugged honeycakes to Cerberus, the three-headed dog who guarded the entrance to the Kingdom of Hades. Cerberus fell asleep and they passed safely. In the Mourning Fields they saw the spirit of Dido, but though Aeneas called to her she did not speak nor even look at him.

Where the road divided, one fork leading to Elysium and the other to Tartarus, they heard the cries of those who had been guilty of grave sin and now endured everlasting punishment. Tantalus, reaching for food and drink that always slipped from his grasp, Ixion bound to his wheel, and Sisyphus forever rolling his stone uphill. Aeneas, led by the Sybil, went on to Elysium, to the beautiful Fields of the Blessed, and there they found his father.

Anchises stretched out his arms in welcome. "Ah, dear son," he said, "you have come. Truly your love for me is strong, for it has brought you safely on this perilous journey." Aeneas would have embraced him, but though he cried, "Let me have your hand, dear Father," and tried to enfold Anchises in his arms, his father's shade slipped from his clasp with no more substance than air.

Anchises now began to tell his son something of the proud empire which would come from the settlement he would found in Italy. And he showed him the ghosts of those who were not yet ready to go to the upper world. Pointing to a dimly lit corner where misty figures moved gently to and fro, he said, "There are the souls of those who will drink from Lethe, the river of forgetfulness, before they are reborn on earth, remembering nothing that has happened before. Some are those who will create the Roman Empire; Romulus from whom the imperial city will take her name, and Julius Caesar, the conqueror, whose realm will reach to the ends of the earth." Then Anchises tried to explain to Aeneas the divine mysteries of life and death, which now, having shed his mortality, he could understand. He showed his son many other strange sights; together they wandered freely amongst the spirits, and over hills and plains, and talked long before Anchises led Aeneas and the Sybil to the ivory gates which opened into the upper world. Before leaving, Aeneas placed the golden branch at the entrance of Queen Persephone's apartments in tribute to her.

When he returned from this astonishing journey, Aeneas went back to his companions. The ships set out once more and the voyagers sailed north, past the island of Circe the enchantress. Another day's journey north, and they reached the mouth of the river Tiber.

They landed and, as provisions had become short and they were very hungry, they quickly gathered wild berries to eat on rounds of bread. After they had eaten the berries and were chewing the flat cakes, Ascanius shouted out, laughing:

"Look! We are eating the plates."

Thus the Harpies' strange prediction did come true! Following an ancient custom, Aeneas poured out libations: to the earth, to the nymphs and streams, to his goddess mother and to Zeus. Lightning flashed and there was thunder in a blue sky, showing that the gods had accepted the offering.

Latinus, king of Latium, as that country was called, had one daughter, Lavinia. Many princes wished to marry her, but it had been foretold that she was to marry a foreign prince. Aeneas sent heralds with a gold cup, along with the scepter, diadem, and robe of King Priam to King Latinus, who then invited him to the palace. Hera was still unwilling to allow Aeneas success even at the end of his quest. She sent Alecto, one of the Furies,

65

to start a quarrel between the Trojan voyagers and the Latins. Alecto took one of the snakes from her head and thrust it at night into the queen's bosom. Queen Amata, waking up in terror, as from a nightmare, screamed to her husband:

"This stranger Aeneas must not marry our daughter!"

"We cannot escape destiny," said King Latinus. "The Sybil of Cumae has prophesied it, and it must be."

In a frenzy, caused by the poison in her blood, the queen rushed out into the woods and, in her deluded state, joined with other women in the rites of the Dionysian mysteries. It was many days before she recovered her reason.

Hera sent Alecto next to Turnus, a wealthy prince in love with the princess Lavinia. She whispered to him:

"This foreigner, Aeneas, wants to take your bride away, so you must attack him."

When Turnus refused, she took off her disguise, and maddened the prince with her snake locks and burning eyes, and the torch she threw at him. In her power at last, he set off with his army against Aeneas.

Hera now made Alecto cause more trouble by driving a tame stag, belonging to the royal herdsman, across Ascanius' path when he was out hunting. Ascanius shot the stag, and in the resulting quarrel some subjects of Latinus were killed, but the king still did nothing, saying only:

"I will not fight a war over this!"

So great Hera herself came down to earth. She went to the city and burst open the gates of Janus. These gates were closed in times of peace, and when they stood open, it meant beyond any doubt that the country was at war.

Aeneas had too few soldiers to fight all those who came against him. But the river god, wearing a long white robe, and with a garland of reeds on his head, appeared to him.

"Aeneas! Take heart, you will overcome your enemies. Tomorrow you will see a great white sow under an ilex tree, as proof that, after thirty years, Ascanius your son will build a new city as was prophesied. And, Aeneas, you must sacrifice to Hera, and pray that she cease her enmity towards you. King Evander, a Greek, will by your ally."

Aeneas sailed on up the river Tiber and on the way saw the sow and her piglets. His mother, Aphrodite, brought him a suit of armor, richly ornamented with shining gold and brass, and a wonderful shield decorated with pictures of the future Rome. These had been made for him by the god Hephaestus, the armorer of Olympus. King Evander came at the head of his army to help Aeneas.

There was fierce war for many months. Then Zeus spoke to Hera, and persuaded her that she could not continue to struggle against Fate. But Hera, though at last willing that Aeneas fulfil his destiny, asked for one favor. Because she hated the name Trojan, it must be heard no more. The Latins and the Trojans should become one people, called Latins. Zeus agreed.

Hera ceased her persecution of Aeneas and it was by her intervention that he overcame Turnus. Thus the war ended, and the story of the Romans began.

When he was settled in the new land, Aeneas built shrines and altars to the gods where worship was conducted according to the old rites and custom. The ceremonies and the stories connected with the Immortals of Olympus were soon adopted by the Latins into their own beliefs, as the connection with Cumae increased and more Greeks came to Latium. But as time passed and new temples were built, and images and statues appeared in sacred precincts, there were changes to accommodate the needs of a developing nation, more practical and less poetic and imaginative than the people of Troy and Greece. And, three hundred years later, when Rome had become a city of consequence, the gods were completely Latinised under their Roman names. Great Zeus, the Father of gods and men was mighty Jove (or Jupiter) the Thunderer, and his consort was re-named Juno; Venus was the goddess of love and Eros, her son, had become the dimpled cherub, Cupid. The Greek god Ares, quarrelsome, and a stirrer-up of strife, but not aggressively warlike, had become Mars, the terrible Roman god of war—a fitting deity for a military and world-conquering people. Demeter was called Ceres and her daughter's name changed to Proserpina, while Dis or Pluto, ruler of the Kingdom of the Dead, was the name given to Hades. Dionysus, the Greek hero-god, shorn of his most important attributes, became Bacchus, the gross god of wine and revelry.

Aeneas did marry Lavinia. He founded the city of Lavinium, which he named in her honor, and he ruled it for three years. After his death, his spirit went, by the will of Zeus, to the Heavenly Plains, and he was succeeded by his son. Ascanius, calling himself Iulus, established Alba Longa as his capital, and in due course mighty Rome was built fifteen miles to the north-west, where it now stands.

So the prophecy for Aeneas, that he should found a "new Troy," was in the end fulfilled.

Norse Myths
and
Medieval Legend

The Death of Balder

retold by Mary Pope Osborne

BALDER was the most beautiful of all the gods. He was so wise and kind and good that all heaven and earth adored him. Many considered him to be the light of the world.

But one night Balder had dark and terrible dreams. He dreamt that he was slain by an unknown enemy. In the morning he met with the gods in their council and told them about his dreams.

Everyone became frightened. They believed Balder's dark dreams were a warning that Balder would soon be harmed. "We must figure out how to protect my beloved son," said Odin.

Some recommended that Balder be guarded at all times. Others urged Odin to send him away. But Balder's mother, Frigg, had the best idea of all.

"I will go out in the nine worlds," the goddess said, "and secure a promise from all of nature that it will never bring harm to Balder."

The gods and goddesses applauded Frigg's plan, and she set out to make the world safe for her son.

Fire and water promised Frigg that they would never hurt Balder. Iron, metal, wood, stones, earth, disease, beasts, birds, and snakes—all assured Frigg that they would never bring harm to Balder.

Finally Frigg returned home, secure in the knowledge that her beloved son was safe.

The gods were so relieved that they played games, mocking fate. They shot arrows at Balder, only to watch their arrows miss their target. They threw stones at him, only to see their stones fall to the ground. They tried to stab Balder with their swords, but their swords bent in midair. They proved again and again that no harm could come to Balder.

All the gods celebrated Balder's invincible power, except for one. Loki, the trickster, grew jealous as he watched the gods at their play.

Loki's jealousy grew until he could bear it no longer. He disguised himself in woman's clothing and found Frigg in her palace.

When she saw Loki, Frigg mistook him for a servant-woman. "What is everyone doing outside?" she called from her spinning wheel. "Why are they laughing and clapping?"

"They're shooting arrows at Balder," said Loki in a high voice. "They're throwing stones at him to prove he cannot be harmed."

"Yes, of course," said Frigg. "That's because wood and stone promised me that they will never hurt him."

"Oh really?" said Loki. "So *all* of nature has promised not to harm your son?"

"Well, not quite all," said Frigg. "I did not bother with one small plant that grows on the eastern side of Valhalla—the mistletoe. It's too young and weak to ever hurt anyone."

"Ah, I see," said Loki. Smiling to himself, he slipped out of Frigg's hall and hurried into the woods east of Valhalla.

Loki searched the forest until he found a piece of mistletoe. He picked the sharp sprig, then rushed to the field where the gods were playing.

Hod, the blind twin of Balder, was standing outside the ring of players.

"Why do you not throw something at Balder?" asked Loki.

"Because I cannot see him," said Hod. "And because I have nothing to throw."

"Oh, but you must show honor to Balder the way the others do," said Loki. "I'll help you shoot him with this dart."

Loki placed the piece of mistletoe in Hod's hand. Then he directed Hod's aim and helped him send the mistletoe toward Balder.

The sharp sprig sailed through the air and lodged in Balder's heart. At once, Balder fell to the ground, dead.

The gods stared in disbelief at Balder's lifeless body. They knew that Loki had wrought this evil, but they could not take vengeance, for their pain and horror were too great.

None grieved more than Odin. With his deep wisdom and knowledge, he alone understood how disastrous was Balder's death. Odin knew that it meant that Ragnarok, the final battle of the world, was close at hand.

Frigg could not let go of her hope that Balder would return. She called the gods together and begged that one of them travel to the land of the dead to find her son and bring him back.

The god Hermod volunteered to go, and Odin gave him Sleipnir for his journey.

The grieving gods carried Balder's body down to the seashore to Balder's dragon-ship, *Ringhorn.*

The gods planned to make Balder's funeral pyre on *Ringhorn.* But when they tried to push the ship into the sea, it would not budge. They sent for a giantess named Hyrrokin, and she arrived on the back of a wolf, snapping reins made of twisted snakes.

Hyrrokin leaned against the ship's prow and with a single shove, she pushed *Ringhorn* into the water.

All the inhabitants of the nine worlds paraded in Balder's funeral procession. First came Odin and Frigg, the Valkyries, and Odin's two ravens. Then came Frey in his chariot drawn by the golden boar, and Freya in her chariot drawn by cats. Then came Thor, Sif, Nanna, Tyr, Heimdall, Bragi, Idun, Njord, Skadi, Gerd, and all the light elves, dark elves, and dwarves. Even the mountain-giants and frost-giants came down from their icy mountains and marched in Balder's funeral procession.

The gods carried Balder onto the ship. When his wife, Nanna, saw the body laid on the pyre, she died of a broken heart and was laid to rest beside her husband.

Odin placed his magic gold ring upon Balder's body, and the funeral pyre was set aflame. Then the burning ship was pushed out to sea.

Meanwhile, the god Hermod was proceeding on his mission to the land of the dead. On the back of Sleipnir, he galloped for nine days and nine nights through deep valleys filled with shadows. Finally he came to a glittering golden bridge.

"Stop! Who are you? Are you dead?" cried a maiden guarding the bridge.

"Not yet," said Hermod. "But I seek one who is—Balder, the fairest of the gods. Have you seen him by chance?"

"Yes," said the maiden. "He and his wife came over this bridge only yesterday. You'll find him if you follow the road to the north."

Hermod crossed the bridge, then traveled until he came to the barred gates of the land of the dead. He spurred Sleipnir, and the magic horse leapt into the air—sailing over the gates without even touching them.

Hermod rode on to the palace. When he entered Hel's home, he found Balder and Nanna sitting in the hall's most honored seats.

Hermod visited with his beloved brother all night. In the morning, he found Hel, the ruler of the dead, and begged her to let Balder and Nanna ride home with him. "The gods cannot stop mourning for this son of Odin," Hermod said.

Hearing those words, Hel's heart softened. "Return to the living," the monster said. "If you find that all beings weep for Balder, I will send him back to you. But if only one creature does not mourn this loss, I will keep him forever."

Before Hermod left, Balder placed Odin's magic ring in his hand. "Take this golden ring back to my father," Balder said. "Tell him I will see him soon."

"And please give this to Frigg," said Nanna, and she gave Hermod a beautiful woven rug.

Hermod said goodbye to Balder and Nanna. Then he rode night and day until he arrived back home.

When Hermod delivered the message from Hel, Odin and Frigg quickly sent messengers out from Asgard to bid the whole world to weep for the death of Balder. All creatures wept as they were asked: gods, goddesses, dwarves, light elves, dark elves, humans—even mountain-giants and frost-giants.

But as the messengers headed back to Asgard, convinced their mission had been successful, they came across a giantess sitting in a cave. She said her name was Thokk, though she was really Loki in disguise.

"Please weep for Balder," said a messenger. "The whole world must weep for him, so he can return from the land of the dead."

"Thokk will only weep with dry tears," Thokk said. "I loved him not. Let Hel keep him for as long as she likes."

And so Balder was not allowed to return to the land of the living. Thus the dark of winter was victorious over the light of the world.

Twilight of the Gods

retold by Mary Pope Osborne

LOKI was punished in the most dreadful way for Balder's death. He was bound to a rock, and a serpent was fastened above his head, its venom dripping onto his face. Loki's faithful wife, Sigyn, sat with him and tried to catch the poison in a basin. But every time she emptied the vessel, poison fell on Loki again, and the earth trembled as he writhed in pain.

When Loki finally broke free from his bondage, he turned completely against the gods and joined the forces of evil. Steering a ship over the seas, he sailed with the sons of Hel. Then, all of the monsters of the world joined them. The wolf Fenrir broke free from his fetters, the Midgard Serpent came from the sea, and the giants from the mountains. Together the evil force marched against Asgard.

Heimdall, the watchman, saw the army crossing the rainbow bridge. He grabbed the mighty trumpet that had never been sounded, and he gave it a long, deep blast.

The terrifying sound wakened all the gods. Odin put on his gold helmet, grabbed his magic spear, and led his warriors into battle.

The gods of Asgard met their foes on a huge plain. Odin attacked the wolf Fenrir. But the wolf devoured him.

Mighty Thor killed the Midgard Serpent, but then fell dead from the serpent's venom.

Frey battled the monster Hel, and lost.

Heimdall fought Loki, and each died by the hand of the other.

The eagle on top of the World Tree screamed with fear. The mighty tree trembled. Mountains crumbled. Seas flooded the land, and hot stars fell from the sky.

Brothers turned against brothers for greed's sake.

Terrible storms raged through the nine worlds.

The wolf Fenrir swallowed the sun, and Moon-Hound finally swallowed the moon. Flames engulfed heaven and earth and all the universe, and all things died—gods, goddesses, men, women, elves, dwarves, monsters, giants, birds, and beasts.

But after the nine worlds had been consumed by fire, the sun brought forth a daughter more lovely than herself. The earth began to turn green again. The eagle soared, and waterfalls flowed in the forests.

Miraculously, some of the gods returned to the world of the living—Balder and his blind twin Hod; and two sons of Thor, Modi and Magni. These gods met on the sunlit plain of Asgard, and they talked about time's morning. They remembered the Midgard Serpent, the wolf Fenrir, and the mighty Odin.

After they talked long and lovingly about the past, they returned to live in heaven, home of the wind.

During the terrible destruction of the universe, two humans had hidden themselves deep in a forest within the World Tree. They were named Life and Eager-for-Life. Now these two came out of hiding, and the dew of early morning served as their food.

From Life and Eager-for-Life came a great multitude of children who spread over the earth.

And thus began a new time and a new world.

Brunhild

by James Baldwin

SIEGFRIED and the harper sat together in the little ship as it lay moored to the sandy shore; and their eyes were turned towards the sea-green castle and its glowing walls, and they looked in vain for any movement, or any sign of wakeful life. Every thing was still. Not a breath of air was stirring. The leaves of the trees hung motionless, as if they, too, were asleep. The great green banner on the tower's top clung around the flagstaff as if it had never fluttered to the breeze. No song of birds, nor hum of insects, came to their ears. There was neither sound nor motion anywhere.

"Play your harp, good Bragi, and awaken all these sleepers," said Siegfried.

Then the harper touched the magic strings, and strains of music, loud and clear, but sweet as a baby's breath, rose up in the still air, and floated over the quiet bay, and across the green meadows which lay around the castle walls; and it was borne upward over the battlements, and among the shining turrets and towers, and was carried far out over the hills, and among the silent trees of the plain. And Bragi sung of the beginning of all things, and of whatsoever is beautiful on the land, or in the sea, or in the sky. And Siegfried looked to see every thing awakened, and quickened into life, as had oft been done before by Bragi's music; but nothing stirred. The sun went down, and the gray twilight hung over sea and land, and the red glow in the castle moat grew redder still; and yet every thing slept. Then Bragi ended his song, and the strings of his harp were mute.

"Music has no charms to waken from sleep like that," he said.

And then he told Siegfried what it all meant; and, to make the story plain, he began by telling of Odin's bright home at Gladsheim and of the many great halls that were there.

One of the halls in Gladsheim is called Valhal. This hall is so large and wide, that all the armies of the earth might move within it. Outside, it is covered with gold and with sun-bright shields. A fierce wolf stands guard before it, and a mountain eagle hovers over it. It has five hundred and forty doors, each large enough for eight hundred heroes to march through abreast. Inside, everything is glittering bright. The rafters are made of spears, and the ceiling is covered with shields, and the walls are decked with war coats. In this hall Odin sets daily a feast for all the heroes that have been slain in battle. These sit at the great table, and eat of the food which Odin's servants have prepared, and drink of the heavenly mead which the Valkyries, Odin's handmaids, bring them.

But the Valkyries have a greater duty. When the battle rages, and swords clash, and shields ring, and the air is filled with shouts and groans and all the din of war, then these maidens hover over the field of blood and death, and carry the slain heroes home to Valhal.

One of Odin's Valkyries was named Brunhild, and she was the most beautiful of all the maidens that chose heroes for his war host. But she was willful too, and did not always obey the All-Father's behests. And when Odin knew that she had sometimes snatched the doomed from death, and sometimes helped her chosen friends to victory, he was very angry. And he drove her away from Gladsheim, and sent her, friendless and poor, to live among the children of men, and to be in all ways like them. But, as she wandered weary and alone over the earth, the good old King of Isenland saw her beauty and her distress, and pity and love moved his heart; and, as he had no children of his own, he took her for his daughter, and made her his heir. And not long afterward he died, and the matchless Brunhild became queen of all the fair lands of Isenland and the hall of Isenstein. When Odin heard of this, he was more angry still; and he sent to Isenstein, and caused Brunhild to be stung with the thorn of Sleep. And he said,—

"She shall sleep until one shall come who is brave enough to ride through fire to awaken her."

And all Isenland slept too, because Brunhild, the Maiden of Spring, lay wounded with the Sleepful thorn.

When Siegfried heard this story, he knew that the land which lay before them was Isenland, and that the castle was Isenstein, and that Brunhild was sleeping within that circle of fire.

"My songs have no power to awaken such a sleeper," said Bragi. "A hero strong and brave must ride through the flame to arouse her. It is for this that I have brought you hither; and here I will leave you, while I sail onwards to brighten other lands with my music."

Siegfried's heart leaped up with gladness; for he thought that here, at last, was a worthy deed for him to do. And he bade his friend Bragi goodby, and stepped ashore; and Greyfell followed him. And Bragi sat at the prow of the ship, and played his harp again; and the sailors plied their oars; and the little vessel moved swiftly out of the bay, and was seen no more. And Siegfried stood alone on the silent, sandy beach.

As he thus stood, the full moon rose white and dripping from the sea; and its light fell on the quiet water, and the sloping meadows, and the green turrets of the castle. And the last notes of Bragi's harp came floating to him over the sea.

Then a troop of fairies came down to dance upon the sands. It was the first sign of life that Siegfried had seen. As the little creatures drew near, he hid himself among the tall reeds which grew close to the shore; for he wished to see them at their gambols, and to listen to their songs. At first, as if half afraid of their own tiny shadows, they danced in silence; but, as the moon rose higher, they grew bolder, and began to sing. And their music was so sweet and soft, that Siegfried forgot almost everything else for the time: they sang of the pleasant summer days, and of cooling shades, and still fountains, and silent birds, and peaceful slumber. And a strange longing for sleep took hold of Siegfried; and his eyes grew heavy, and the sound of the singing seemed dim and far away. But just as he was losing all knowledge of outward things, and his senses seemed moving in a dream, the fairies stopped dancing, and a little brown elf came up from the sea, and saluted the queen of the tiny folk.

"What news bring you from the great world beyond the water?" asked the queen.

"The prince is on his way hither," answered the elf.

"And what will he do?"

"If he is brave enough, he will awaken the princess, and arouse the drowsy people of Isenstein; for the Norns have said that such a prince shall surely come."

"But he must be the bravest of men ere he can enter the enchanted castle," said the queen; "for the wide moat is filled with flames, and no faint heart will ever dare battle with them."

"But I will dare!" cried Siegfried; and he sprang from his hiding place, forgetful of the little folk, who suddenly flitted away, and left him alone upon the beach. He glanced across the meadows at the green turrets glistening in the mellow moonlight, and then at the flickering flames around the castle walls, and he resolved that on the morrow he would at all hazards perform the perilous feat.

In the morning, as soon as the gray dawn appeared, he began to make ready for his difficult undertaking. But, when he looked again at the red flames, he began to hesitate. He paused, uncertain whether to wait for a sign and for help from the All-Father, or whether to go straightaway to the castle, and, trusting in his good armor alone, try to pass through the burning moat. While he thus stood in doubt, his eyes were dazzled by a sudden flash of light. He looked up. Greyfell came dashing across the sands; and from his long mane a thousand sunbeams gleamed and sparkled in the morning light. Siegfried had never seen the wondrous creature so radiant; and as the steed stood by him in all his strength and beauty he felt new hope and courage, as if Odin himself had spoken to him. He hesitated no longer, but mounted the noble horse; and Greyfell bore him swiftly over the plain, and paused not until he had reached the brink of the burning moat.

Now, indeed, would Siegfried's heart have failed him, had he not been cheered by the sunbeam presence of Greyfell. For filling the wide, deep ditch, were angry, hissing flames, which, like a thousand serpent tongues, reached out, and felt here and there, for what they might devour; and ever and anon they took new forms, and twisted and writhed like fiery snakes, and then they swirled in burning coils high over the castle walls. Siegfried stopped not a moment. He spoke the word, and boldly the horse with his rider dashed into the fiery lake; and the vile flames fled in shame and dismay before the pure sunbeam flashes from Greyfell's mane. And, unscorched and unscathed, Siegfried rode through the moat, and through the wide open gate, and into the castle yard.

The gatekeeper sat fast asleep in his lodge, while the chains and the heavy key with which, when awake, he was wont to make the great gate fast, lay rusting at his feet; and neither he, nor the sentinels on the ramparts above, stirred or awoke at the sound of Greyfell's clattering hoofs. As Siegfried passed from one part of the castle to another, many strange sights met his eyes. In the stables the horses slumbered in their stalls, and the grooms lay snoring by their sides. The birds sat sound asleep on their nests beneath the eaves. The watchdogs, with fast-closed eyes, lay stretched at full length before the open doors. In the garden the fountain no longer played, the half-laden bees had gone to sleep among the blossoms of the apple trees, and the flowers themselves had forgotten to open their petals to the sun. In the kitchen the cook was dozing over the half-baked meats in front of the smoldering fire; the butler was snoring in the pantry; the dairymaid was quietly napping among the milk pans; and even the house flies had gone to sleep over the crumbs of sugar on the table. In the great banquet room a thousand knights, overcome with slumber, sat silent at the festal board; and their chief, sitting on the dais, slept, with his half-emptied goblet at his lips.

Siegfried passed hurriedly from room to room and from hall to hall, and cast but one hasty glance at the strange sights which met him at every turn; for he knew that none of the drowsy ones in that spacious castle could be awakened until he had aroused the Princess Brunhild. In the grandest hall of the palace he found her. The peerless maiden, most richly dight, reclined upon a couch beneath a gold-hung canopy; and her attendants, the ladies of the court, sat near and around her. Sleep held fast her eyelids, and her breathing was so gentle, that, but for the blush upon her cheeks, Siegfried would have thought her dead. For long, long years had her head thus lightly rested on that gold-fringed pillow; and in all that time neither her youth had faded, nor her wondrous beauty waned.

Siegfried stood beside her. Gently he touched his lips to that matchless forehead; softly he named her name,—

"Brunhild!"

The charm was broken. Up rose the peerless princess in all her queen-like beauty; up rose the courtly ladies round her. All over the castle, from cellar to belfry tower, from the stable to the banquet-hall, there was a sudden awakening,—a noise of hurrying feet and mingled voices, and sounds which had long been strangers to the halls of Isenstein. The watchman on the tower, and the sentinels on the ramparts, yawned, and would not believe they had been asleep; the porter picked up his keys, and hastened to lock the long-forgotten gates; the horses neighed in their stalls; the watchdogs barked at the sudden hubbub; the birds, ashamed at having allowed the sun to find them napping, hastened to seek their food in the meadows; the servants hurried here and there, each intent upon his duty; the warriors in the banquet hall clattered their knives and plates, and began again their feast; and their chief dropped his goblet, and rubbed his eyes, and wondered that sleep should have overtaken him in the midst of such a meal.

And Siegfried, standing at an upper window, looked out over the castle walls; and he saw that the flames no longer raged in the moat, but that it was filled with clear sparkling water from the fountain which played in the garden. And the south wind blew gently from the sea, bringing from afar the sweetest strains of music from Bragi's golden harp; and the breezes whispered among the trees, and the flowers opened their petals to the sun, and birds and insects made the air melodious with their glad voices. Then Brunhild, radiant with smiles, stood by the hero's side, and welcomed him kindly to Isenland and to her green-towered castle of Isenstein.

The Sword in the Stone

retold by Rosemary Sutcliff

CHRISTMAS came, and with it a great gathering who thronged the abbey church, while those for whom there was no room inside crowded the churchyard to watch the distant glimmer of candles and hear the singing and share in the Mass as best they could through the great West door which stood open wide. And when Mass was done, and they turned to go, and those within the church began to come out, suddenly there began a murmur of wonder which spread out and out through the throng like the ripples spreading when a trout leaps in a pool.

For there in the midst of the churchyard, none having seen it come, was a great block of marble, and rooted in the block, an anvil; and standing with its point bedded in the anvil and through into the marble beneath, a naked sword. And round the block was written in letters of gold, clear in the winter sunshine, *"Who so pulleth out this sword from this stone and anvil is true-born King of all Britain."*

Then one after another the lesser kings and the lords and at last even the simple knights of their followings began to try to draw the sword from the stone. But none succeeded; and far on towards evening when the last had tried, there stood the sword, as firmly set as it had been at the first moment of its appearing; and the crowd stood around, weary and baffled, with their breath smoking in the cold air.

"He is not here, who shall draw this blade," said the Archbishop, "but God shall send him in good time. Hear now my counsel: let messengers be sent out the length and breadth of the land, telling of this wonder, and bidding all who would seek to win the sword and with it the kingdom come to a great tournament to be held here in London upon Candlemas Day. And meanwhile let a silken pavilion be set up to shelter the wonder, and let ten knights be chosen to stand guard over it night and day. And so maybe God shall send us our King that day."

So the messengers rode out on the fastest horses that could be found, carrying the word far and wide through the land, as though it had been a flaming torch. And at last it came to the castle of Sir Ector in the Wild Forest on the fringes of Wales.

Now Sir Ector was a quiet man, and growing old; but his son Kay had been made a knight at the feast of Hallowmas only a few months before, and felt his knighthood bright and untried upon him, and longed like every other young knight in the kingdom to try his fortune at drawing the wonderful sword.

His father laughed at him, but kindly. "Do you think, then, that you are the rightful High King of all Britain?"

Kay, who could not bear to be laughed at, flushed scarlet. "I am not such a fool as that, Father; but this will be the greatest and most splendid tournament that has ever been seen, and it would be a fine thing to prove myself there."

"It would so," said Sir Ector. "Well, I remember when my knighthood was three months old I would have felt the same."

Now Arthur, who was but just turned fifteen, was standing by and listening to the talk of his foster kin; a tall big-boned lad with a brown skin and mouse-fair hair and eyes that would be kind and quiet when he was older but just now were full of eager lights at the thought of the great tournament and the magic sword. And Kay turned on him impatiently: "You heard! We're going to London for the tournament! Oh, don't just stand there like a shock of wet barley! You're my squire—go and get my armour ready or we'll never be in London by Candlemas!"

Arthur looked at him for a moment as though he would have liked to hit him. But then he thought, It is only because his knighthood is so new upon him. When he has had time to grow used to it, he will be different. He was used to making excuses to himself for Kay. And he went to see to his foster brother's armour, although he knew that Candlemas was as yet a long way off and there was plenty of time.

They reached London on a snowy Candlemas Eve, and found the city buzzing like a hive of bees about to swarm, so full of nobles and knights and their squires and trains of servants that at first it did not seem that they would be able to find lodgings for the night. But they found a corner in an inn at last; and next morning set out through the crowded streets to the tournament ground. All the world seemed going the same way, and it was as though they were carried along by a river in spate. The snow had been swept from the tournament field outside the city walls, so that it was like a green lake in the white-bound countryside; and all round the margin of the lake were the painted stands for the onlookers and the pavilions of those who were to take part; blue and emerald and vermilion, chequered and striped; and the crowds were gathering thicker every moment, and all among them horses were being walked up and down, their breath steaming on the cold air. And it all seemed to Arthur, fresh from his forest country, to be as beautiful and confusing as some kind of dream.

But just as they reached the tournament ground, Kay discovered that, with too much eagerness and too much anxiety, he had left his sword behind him at the inn.

"That is my blame," Arthur said quickly. "I am your squire, I should have seen that you were properly armed."

And Kay, who had been going to say that same thing himself, could only say, "It's over late to be worrying as to whose blame it is. Ride back quickly and fetch it and come on after us."

So Arthur turned his cob and began to ride back the way they had come. But now he was going against the flow of the people, and when at last he managed to reach the inn, it was fast locked and shuttered, and all the people of the house were gone to watch the jousting.

Now what am I to do? thought Arthur. There will be jests and laughter if Kay comes to the tournament without a sword—and yet how am I to get one for him in this strange city and with so little time to spare?

And as if in answer, there came clearly into his mind the picture of a sword that he had seen earlier that morning, standing upright in a stone in the garth of the great abbey church close by. I wonder what it is there for, and if it lifts out of the stone? he thought, and found that he was already urging his cob that way.

For the strange thing was that in the moment that he thought of the sword in the stone, he forgot its meaning and why the tournament had been called. Maybe that had something to do with the passing beggarman whose strange golden eyes had met his for an instant as he turned his cob from the locked door of the inn; for assuredly if he had not forgotten, he would never have thought of trying to get it out of the stone, even for Kay his foster brother . . .

When he reached the garth of the abbey church he dismounted and hitched his cob to the gate and went in. The fresh snow lay among the tombstones, and in the midst of the tall black sentinel towers of the yew trees the pavilion glowed crimson as a rose at Midsummer; and the sword stood lonely in its anvil on the great stone, for even the ten knights were gone to the jousting.

Then Arthur took the sword two-handed by its quillions. There was golden writing on the stone, but he did not stop to read it. The sword seemed to thrill under his touch as a harp thrills in response to its master's hand. He felt strange, as though he were on the point of learning some truth that he had forgotten before he was born. The thin winter sunlight was so piercing-bright that he seemed to hear it; a high white music in his blood.

He drew the sword from the anvil in one familiar-seeming movement as though from a well-oiled sheath. And he ran back to the gate where his cob waited, and made all haste back towards the tournament field. The crowds in the streets were thinning now, and in only a short while he reached the place where Sir Kay had turned aside, sitting his horse in a fret, to wait for him.

"This is not my sword," Kay said, as Arthur thrust it into his hand.

"I could not get in, the place was locked up—I came on this one by chance, in the abbey garth, sticking in a great stone—"

Kay looked at the sword again. He was suddenly very white. Then he wheeled his horse and began thrusting through the crowd towards Sir Ector, who had ridden on ahead. Arthur followed hard behind.

"Sir," said Kay, when he reached his father, "here is the sword out of the stone; here in my hand. It must be that I am the true High King of Britain."

But Sir Ector looked at his son steadily and kindly, and from him to Arthur and back again, and said, "Let us go back to the church."

And when the three of them had dismounted and gone into the great echoing church, all glimmering with tapers for Candlemas, he made Kay put his hand on the Bible, and said, "Now tell me in all truth, how you came by this sword."

And Kay turned from white to red, and said, "My brother Arthur brought it to me."

Sir Ector turned to his foster son, and asked, "How came you by this sword?"

Arthur, troubled because he could not think what Kay had meant when he said that he must be High King of Britain, but still not remembering, said, "Kay sent me to fetch his sword, but the lodging was empty and locked up, and I could not think what to do—and then I thought me of this sword in the church garth, and it was serving no useful purpose there, while Kay needed a sword, so I pulled it out and brought it to him."

"Were there any knights standing by, who saw you do the thing?" asked Sir Ector.

Arthur shook his head. "No one."

"Then," said Sir Ector, "put the sword back in its place." And when Arthur had done so, Sir Ector tried to draw it out again, and could not shift it. And then at his order Kay tried, but with no better success. "Now do you draw it forth again, Fosterling," he said. And Arthur, greatly wondering what all the to-do was about, drew the sword again, as easily as he had done the first time.

Then Sir Ector knelt down before him, and bowed his head, and Kay also, though more slowly; and Arthur, beginning to remember and trying not to, and suddenly more afraid than ever he had been in his life before, cried out, "Father—Kay—why do you kneel to me?"

"Because you have drawn the sword from the stone, and it is ordained by God himself that none shall do that save he who is rightfully High King of Britain."

"Not me!" Arthur said. "Oh, not me!"

"I never knew whose son you were when Merlin brought you to me for fostering," said Sir Ector. "But I know now that you were of higher blood than I thought you."

"Get up!" said Arthur. "Oh sir, get up! I cannot bear that you should kneel to me, you who have been my father all these years!" And when Sir Ector would not, he dropped on to his knees also, to be on a level with the old man again.

"I kneel to my liege lord," said Sir Ector. "I will serve you in all things and keep true faith with you. Only be a gentle lord to me, and to Kay your foster brother."

"Kay shall be Seneschal of all my lands, if I be King indeed," said Arthur. "And how could I be any but a gentle lord to you whom I love. And for the rest—I will serve God and the realm of Britain with the best that is in me. Only get up now, for indeed I cannot bear it!" And he covered his face with his hands and wept as though his heart would break.

Then Sir Ector and Sir Kay got up, and Arthur himself last of all; and they went to the Archbishop and told him of what had happened, and as the word spread, knights and nobles came pouring up from the tournament ground, demanding that they should also try for the sword, as was their right; and Arthur set it back into the stone, and one after another, they tried without avail.

Yet they would not accept that a boy not yet come to his knighthood, and with no proof of his fathering, should be king over them. And so the Archbishop ordained another gathering at Easter, and then yet another at Pentecost, and to each of these the great lords swarmed in to try again; but none could draw the sword save Arthur. And at last the people cried that they were weary of this striving, and would have Arthur for their king.

Then Arthur took his sword across both hands and offered it before the altar in the abbey church, and received his knighthood of the Archbishop. And that same day the Archbishop set the crown upon his head.

The royal circlet pressed down upon his forehead with all the weight of the fear and bewilderment that had been with him ever since he had first drawn the sword from the stone; so that it was all he could do to hold his head high as he turned to confront the knights and nobles who crowded the body of the great church. And then he became aware that as the Archbishop Dubricius stood beside him on his right, somebody else was with him on his left—a tall man in a dark mantle, with hair on his head like black ruffled feathers. Arthur did not know who he was; but it was clear that the Archbishop knew, and Sir Ector his foster father standing close by, and many others in the church, and that even those who did not know felt the power that flowed from him like light from a torch or the spreading quiver in the air from a lightly tapped drum.

There was faint stirring and shifting among the crowd, and a whisper began to go round, "Merlin! It is Merlin!" "He was with Utha and Ambrosius; often I saw him!" "It is Merlin, the magician!"

And one of the great lords, leader of many fighting men, who had had high hopes of his own claim to the crown, shouted, "It is Merlin and not God who has chosen for us this beardless boy to be our new king!"

And another joined him, as hound bays after hound, "Aye, it is nought but Merlin's dream-weaving, this magic of a sword in a stone!"

Standing so still that save for his back-falling sleeve, not a fold of his dark mantle stirred, Merlin raised his arm, and silence flowed out from him the length and breadth of the church. Only a faint murmur seemed to hang between the pillars and in the emptiness under the high arched roof like the echo of the sea in a shell. And into the silence, Merlin lifted up his voice and spoke.

"Listen now, oh people of Britain, and you shall know the truth. Truth that has been hidden from you many years until the time should come for you to hear it. Here stands your High King, true and rightful son of Utha Pendragon and his Queen Igraine; born to be the greatest king that Britain has ever known, born to drive back the enemies of the realm further even than the Pendragon drove them in his day. Born to bring that brightness between the Dark and the Dark that men shall remember beyond the mists of time and call the Kingdom of Logres. He was God's choice, not mine, but it was given to me to know him, before he was born, before even his king-star hung in the sky, and to do what must be done to bring him safely to this day!"

And standing still with his hand raised, he told the whole story of the dragon in the sky, and of Arthur's birth, and how he had taken the child and given him to Sir Ector's fosterage to be brought up in safety from the troubles that followed his father's death, until the time came for him to take the crown and the sword.

When he had done, he lowered his hand, and, as though it was a signal, the uproar broke out again, but now it swelled into a roar of acclamation; and men were shouting, "Utha's son! Utha's son!"

And in the midst of the shouting the tall man in the dark cloak turned his head and looked at the boy beside him; and Arthur found himself looking back, into strange golden eyes that were not like the eyes of any mortal man that he had met before. And yet as he looked into them he seemed to remember for a moment a beggar by the inn doorway that Candlemas morning that now seemed a lifetime ago, and a stray harper playing by the fire in the hall of his old home, and a travelling tinker, and a wounded soldier making his way home from the wars. The rags of memory were gone before he could lay hold of them. But with them, all the fear and bewilderment went from his mind. The sorrow for the loss of his old life remained, but it no longer mattered. Suddenly his head was clear and his heart strong within him; and he knew that whatever he had to do in this new life, he could do it.

"Speak to them," said Merlin, beside him.

And Arthur spoke, lifting up his voice clear for all the knights and nobles in the great church, and the people thronging beyond the open door, and for all the people of Britain. "I am your King! I will keep faith with you. Do you keep faith with me! When this feast of Pentecost is over let us gather our forces, and together we will drive back the Sea-wolves and the men of the North who ravage these lands! We will free the realm of the strife and the fire and the sword that have torn it apart in the years since my father's death. You and I together, let us make this a good land, where men do not rule only because they are strong, but where men are strong for the Right, none the less! Give me your love and your faithkeeping, oh people of Britain, and I will give you mine through all the days of my life!"

And there was no more shouting and acclamation; only a deep silence in the great church. But it was a good silence; and the tall man with the golden eyes smiled, as one that is well content.

Myths From Around the World

Apsu and Tiamat the Creators

retold by Virginia Hamilton

WHAT was on high had not been named. And firm ground below had not been called. There was but Apsu the begetter, the fresh and sweet-water sea. And there was Tiamat, the salt-sea waters. They mingled as a single body and soul.

There was no hut of reeds. No marsh lands. When there was Apsu and Tiamat, and nothing else, they created the great gods.

They brought the gods Lahmu and Lahamu into being. And for ages these two grew and grew.

The gods Anshar and Kishar were formed next, and they grew even taller. The god Anu was their son. He was equal to his father, Anshar.

Anu brought the god, Ea, into being. Ea was wise, understanding, and strong. He was even mightier than his grandfather, Anshar. There were none to rival him among the gods.

The god brothers banded together in the sweet and salt waters as more of them came into being. They surged back and forth. This bothered Tiamat. Some say she was a dragon. The god sons made her moody with their noise and laughter.

Apsu could not stop the brother gods, and Tiamat could not speak to them, for they were too overbearing. Apsu decided to destroy them so that he and Tiamat could have peace.

"What? Should we unmake what we have made?" Tiamat asked. Her mood was dark now. "Their ways are awful, these gods, but let us act kindly!"

Apsu continued to plan evil against the gods, his sons. But the gods heard what was plotted. They became silent, all but one. He was Ea, the all-wise.

Ea made a spell. He spoke the magic, and he put it in the deep of the fresh water that was Apsu. His spell made Apsu fall sound asleep, and then Ea killed him.

Ea and Damkina, his wife, dwelled in splendor in this watery place of fate; they called it the Apsu. And in the heart of the Apsu was created the majestic god, Marduk. It was Ea and Damkina's doing. They were the father and mother.

Marduk looked like a god of gods for all time. His eyes flashed and sparked. Leader that he was, he walked like a Lord of the

Ages. When Ea first saw him, his heart was filled with rejoicing. He said Marduk was perfect and to be praised as the most high god.

Marduk had four eyes and four ears. When his lips moved, the fire blazed from within. His eyes scanned everything. He was fearless and radiant. He was best and tallest, boldest, and brave.

"My little son, my little son!" exclaimed Ea. "My son, the sun! Sun of the Heavens!" Marduk was the sun of all.

The god Anu then made the four winds. They, in turn, brought waves and foam to Tiamat's waters. Diving down, Anu filled his palm and created dirt. Waves stirred up the dirt.

Tiamat did not like being upset and so disturbed. She moved and moved, day and night. The gods could not rest.

"We cannot sleep," they said. "You let Apsu be killed and did not stay at his side. Now there are four winds. You are alone. We cannot rest. You do not love us!"

"Let us make monsters, then!" Tiamat said.

She who could fashion all things gave birth to monster serpents. She made roaring dragons, bloodless and filled with poison. And she crowned them with halos, so they would look like gods. Looking upon them, the onlooker would perish.

Tiamat created the Viper, the Dragon, and the Sphinx, the great Lion, the Mad Dog, and the Scorpion Man. She created demons, the Dragon-fly, the Centaur. There were eleven of them that she made herself. And among these creatures she made Kingu.

Tiamat made Kingu the chief of the monsters, and they would battle now against the fairer gods—Anshar and Ea, and Anu. They would avenge the death of Apsu.

Anu went to stand against Tiamat and her terrible dark brood.

But Anu could not withstand her. He had to retreat.

Then Ea called his son, Marduk. And Lord Marduk was pleased. He prepared himself and stood before the fair god Anshar.

"I will accomplish all that is in your heart," said Marduk. "I will be your avenger and slay Tiamat. But you must make me supreme. From now on, my words will fix the destinies of the gods. And whatever I create will remain unchanged."

So the gods agreed to grant Marduk kingship of the universe. But first they spread the starry robe of the night sky in their midst.

The gods said to Marduk, "By your word, make the robe vanish." Marduk spoke in words of sun and light, and the robe vanished. "By your word," said the gods, "let the robe appear again." Marduk spoke in the words of night and stars, and the robe was seen again.

The gods rejoiced.

"Marduk is King!" they said.

Then Marduk made ready for battle. He took up his scepter the gods had given him, his royal ring, and his thunderbolt. He took up his bow and arrow and his club. He placed lightning in front of him and made his body full of flame. He made a net to trap Tiamat.

The four winds helped him so that she could not get away. He brought evil winds, whirlwinds and hurricanes, to stir up the waters of Tiamat. He rode his terrifying chariot of rage. To this he tied his four-team: the Killer, the Crusher, Unyielder, and Fleet.

Lord Marduk went forward wrapped in armor, his head dressed in a turbaned halo. He went to face fierce Tiamat. He had magic in his mouth and a root against poison in his hand. The gods milled all around him. He went forward and looked inside Tiamat.

"You have put Kingu in place of the rule of Anu and against Anshar, king of the gods. Stand up now and fight me!"

Tiamat cried out in fury. She cast her spells. The Lord Marduk spread his net to entrap her. She screamed out a poison. Then Marduk unleashed an evil wind. Tiamat spread her mouth to eat him. He drove the evil wind down her waterspout. Marduk let loose his arrow; it cut Tiamat in half.

Lord Marduk stood above Tiamat as she died. Her monsters and demons trembled with terror. Marduk captured them and smashed their weapons. When these dark gods cried out, Marduk crushed them underfoot.

Turning back to cold Tiamat, Marduk raised one half of her on high. He made it the heavens. Then he surveyed the Apsu of Ea, his father, and the deep waters. The other half of dead Tiamat he made the Earth, as a great abode above the Apsu.

Marduk the Victorious made the days of the year, and the order of the planets, and the moods of the moon. He made constellations of the gods.

He stood still for an age, having a strange and wondrous thought. He told Ea, his father, "I will have blood all around us. I shall frame it with bone. I shall build a creature.

"*Man* shall be his name!" spoke Marduk. "Oh, Man! You shall serve all of the gods."

And so it came to pass. The Lord God Marduk spoke it. He let there be Man and thus freed the gods from eternal labor.

The Hungry Goddess

told by Olga Loya

ONCE long, long ago the Aztec gods lived high up. In those days there was no sky and there was no earth. There was only water and water and water. There was water from nowhere to nowhere.

Among the gods, there lived a goddess. She was called La Diosa Hambrienta, the Hungry Goddess, because she had eyes and mouths all over her body. She had mouths and eyes at her elbows, wrists, ankles, waist—everywhere. She was always hungrily trying to see what was happening. She was always trying to eat, and she was always crying out, *"Tengo hambre*, tengo hambre."*

All day long she would wail, *"Tengo hambre."*

All night long she would say, *"Tengoooo hambre!"*

Day in and day out, she called out, *"Tengo hambre."*

Finally all the gods went to the two most powerful gods of all and said, "Por favor, can't you do something? The woman is always crying. We can't sleep. We can't think! She's always saying, *'Tengo hambre.'"*

Now the two most powerful gods were Quetzalcoatl and Tezcatlipoca. The gods called Quetzalcoatl the Plumed Serpent because he wore beautifully flowing feathers of many colors and he walked with a stick carved in the shape of a serpent. He dressed in white. He wore gold hoop earrings, bells around his legs, and pearls on his sandals. He also wore a mask shaped like a bird's head called the Wind Mask. With that mask, he could blow the wind for a long distance. Thus, he was also known as the Wind God and the God of Light.

Tezcatlipoca dressed in black. He wore rattlesnake rattles around his legs. He was sometimes called the God of Smoking Mirror because he wore an obsidian mirror—made of black volcanic glass—on his foot, with which he could see everything that was happening in the world. Tezcatlipoca's other name was the God of Darkness.

Quetzalcoatl and Tezcatlipoca talked and talked. Finally they decided they would take La Diosa Hambrienta to the water; maybe the water would calm her. So they flew down to the water

---

*__Tengo hambre__ [tän′gō äm′brä]: Spanish for "I'm hungry."

to see if there was anything there for the goddess to eat. Quetzalcoatl blew with his Wind Mask. He blew and blew, and the water went this way and that way. They could find nothing at all.

They flew up to La Diosa Hambrienta and carried her down to the water. On the way down, she continued to cry, *"Tengo hambre! Tengo hambre!"*

They put her on the water. She was silent. She was floating so quietly, so calmly.

The gods said, "Ah, she is now happy."

But no, she started to cry out again: *"Tengooo haaambreee."*

Quetzalcoatl and Tezcatlipoca became quite upset. They transformed themselves into huge serpents and took hold of La Diosa Hambrienta. One god took her right hand and left foot and the other took her left hand and right foot. They started to pull and pull. But the goddess was very strong. She fought them long and hard. It was the most difficult fight the gods had ever fought. As they continued to struggle, they accidentally snapped her in half.

Quetzalcoatl and Tezcatlipoca were very surprised—and very sorry. They took the bottom half—from the waist to the feet—of La Diosa Hambrienta to the other gods and said, "Look what we have done!"

"What a shame," the other gods said. "Wait, we will use this half of the hungry woman and it shall be the sky." That is how the sky came to be.

The gods looked at the goddess's top half. "Poor thing," they said. "Look how unhappy she is. What can we do? Let us make her happy."

So they transformed her hair into the forest. Her skin became the pastures; her eyes became the lakes, the rivers and the ocean. Her mouth became the caves; her shoulders became the mountains. She became Mother Earth—the earth we live on to this day.

All the gods said, "Ah, now she will be happy!"

But no! She again started to wail, *"Tengooo haaambre, tengooo haaambre!"*

To this day La Diosa Hambrienta, Mother Earth, is still hungry and thirsty. When it rains, she swallows all the water. If a tree falls and dies, she eats it. If a flower wilts and dies, she eats it. When anything goes into the earth, she eats it. She is always hungry.

Sometimes when the wind is blowing late at night, if you listen very carefully, you might still hear her calling, *"Tengo haaambree, tengo haaambreee."*

The First People

retold by Mercedes Dorson and Jeanne Wilmot

LONG, long ago, during celestial times when the spirits lived in the skies and the ancestors of the Indians inhabited the world of darkness under the earth, there were two sorcerers, Aroteh and Tovapod. They lived on the earth where together they shared a hut by a clearing in which maize, sweet potatoes, papayas, and peanuts were as plentiful as cassava, guava, wild game, and land tortoises. The plants grew naturally and abundantly so daily, Aroteh and Tovapod husked the corn and shelled the peanuts in order to maintain an ample supply. The corn was kept in small mounds around the hut and the peanuts were held in dried calabash gourds. Aroteh and Tovapod ate well and had each other for company.

One day, Aroteh noticed that the harvest was being depleted. He spoke to Tovapod about the problem and suggested that they lie in wait to ambush the thief. That night they took turns watching so that one could sleep while the other guarded the corn near the hut. Tovapod crouched patiently under the shadow of a jacaranda tree as dawn neared. He did not want to be seen circling the periphery of the hut. Suddenly he heard movement near him. Watching for the pillager, he was astonished to see an arm reaching up behind one of the calabashes. When a beautiful woman rose out of the steamy first light of the morning, she was so striking, Tovapod believed he was seeing perfection for the first time. She calmly moved over to the nearest mound of corn, but when she heard Tovapod shifting his weight, she stood still. Tovapod did not move. Since she heard nothing further, she returned to the business of gathering corn and guava. Then, as suddenly as she had materialized, she disappeared.

After a few moments Tovapod carefully approached the area where the mysterious woman had been. Nearing the very spot, he discovered an even more remarkable occurrence: human arms were reaching out through a small hole in the earth. He thought that probably only very small people could pass through the hole because there was an immense boulder closing off an opening to what appeared to be a subterranean world.

The arms drew back when Tovapod kneeled to try to enlarge the opening. He dug and dug but to no avail. The boulder settled more firmly over the hole. Finally he ran in to awaken Aroteh. Tovapod told Aroteh about the world they never knew existed. He asked Aroteh to speak to the Wind for help. Tovapod wanted the Wind to gather her strength and blow against his back so he would have the power to push the boulder out of the way.

The Wind agreed to blow against Tovapod's back, so on the first attempt Tovapod and Aroteh were easily able to shove the boulder away from the hole. The sorcerers were amazed by what they saw. Beneath the earth lived hundreds of people with fingers webbed together like ducks' feet, protruding chins and horns all over the sides and tops of their heads, long noses, and sharp teeth. Some were ugly, some had tails, and some looked more like animals than people.

Aroteh called to the people to hurry out through the opening while Tovapod supported the weight of the heavy boulder. The Wind remained at Tovapod's back as a silent partner. Time passed and hundreds of people poured out of the crevasse. But the commotion mounted as many of them, clutching their possessions, rushed to leave the darkness.

Aroteh wondered who the people were and how they had survived below the earth. They had been suffering from great hunger for many generations. All that the people had available to eat were wretched palm fruits. Then one night, one of them discovered the hole in the earth. The beautiful woman and some of the children were the only ones slender enough to pass through the opening. Night after night, they would forage for the others, bringing back armloads of cassava, yams, and bananas before the day's early light, when they would return below to their hungry friends and families.

The people had been deprived for so long that they were now desperate. In their eagerness to enter the new world, they pushed each other out of the way as they neared the opening. The quarreling slowed them down, which worried Tovapod, for he feared he would lose control of the boulder. The boulder was weighing on him, and the Wind would lose her strength eventually. As Tovapod worried, out of the chaos the beautiful woman suddenly appeared. He almost let go of the boulder. In the woman's haste to reach the surface, however, she left something below. Tovapod tried to tell her not to return underground, but the woman could not understand his unfamiliar language. The woman started back to retrieve her possessions and was pushed into the darkness by another person seeking the new world.

The exhausted Tovapod withstood the weight of the boulder for as long as he could, but eventually he weakened. He kept searching the faces of the emerging people for the beautiful woman. She was nowhere to be seen. The Wind slowed down, and Tovapod could not manage the weight alone. He looked into the hole one last time and tried to find the woman. Still she did not reappear. Tovapod had seen that the woman had no webbing or horns anyplace on her body. She was able to move with more ease and dexterity than the rest of her people. Tovapod was disappointed to lose the woman whom he thought would be a good model for the others, but he had no choice. He had to let the boulder slide back into place and cover the hole completely.

Aroteh had already brought out straw mats for the people to rest and benches for them to sit. Tovapod's job was to shape the people's teeth, fingers, and toes because they were too sharp, and he did not want them to hurt each other. He cut off their horns and antlers, snipped off their tails, and pared down the area between their webbed fingers and toes so they could move more easily. It was a long and arduous process. Every time the sun was almost setting, Aroteh pushed it back up so that it would not get dark. They needed a long day to complete their tasks.

After everyone was fixed, Tovapod taught the people how to sing. First he taught them melody, and then he taught them language. Some people remained in the area near the original clearing, and others wandered far away where there was more space. Tovapod stretched the earth and the woods to make enough room for everyone to fit. As the people moved farther and farther away from each other, they separated into individual tribes and created their own languages and songs.

From Bumba

by Maria Leach

IN the beginning, in the dark, there was nothing but water. And Bumba was alone.

One day Bumba was in terrible pain. He retched and strained and vomited up the sun. After that light spread over everything. The heat of the sun dried up the water until the black edges of the world began to show. Black sandbanks and reefs could be seen. But there were no living things.

Bumba vomited up the moon and then the stars, and after that the night had its own light also.

Still Bumba was in pain. He strained again and nine living creatures came forth: the leopard named Koy Bumba, and Pongo Bumba the crested eagle, the crocodile, Ganda Bumba, and one little fish named Yo; next, old Kono Bumba, the tortoise, and Tsetse, the lightning, swift, deadly, beautiful like the leopard, then the white heron, Nyanyi Bumba, also one beetle, and the goat named Budi.

Last of all came forth men. There were many men, but only one was white like Bumba. His name was Loko Yima.

The creatures themselves then created all the creatures. The heron created all the birds of the air except the kite. He did not make the kite. The crocodile made serpents and the iguana. The goat produced every beast with horns. Yo, the small fish, brought forth all the fish of all the seas and waters. The beetle created insects.

Then the serpents in their turn made grasshoppers, and the iguana made the creatures without horns.

Then the three sons of Bumba said they would finish the world. The first, Nyonye Ngana, made the white ants; but he was not equal to the task, and died of it. The ants, however, thankful for life and being, went searching for black earth in the depths of the world and covered the barren sands to bury and honor their creator.

Chonganda, the second son, brought forth a marvelous living plant from which all the trees and grasses and flowers and plants in the world have sprung. The third son, Chedi Bumba, wanted something different, but for all his trying made only the bird called the kite.

Of all the creatures Tsetse, lightning, was the only trouble-maker. She stirred up so much trouble that Bumba chased her into the sky. Then mankind was without fire until Bumba showed the people how to draw fire out of trees. "There is fire in every tree," he told them, and showed them how to make the firedrill and liberate it. Sometimes today Tsetse still leaps down and strikes the earth and causes damage.

When at last the work of creation was finished, Bumba walked through the peaceful villages and said to the people, "Behold these wonders. They belong to you." Thus from Bumba, the Creator, the First Ancestor, came forth all the wonders that we see and hold and use, and all the brotherhood of beasts and man.

How Grandmother Spider Named the Clans

retold by Joseph Bruchac

AFTER Tawa, the Sky God, and Grandmother Spider had made Earth and all of the things upon it, Tawa went back up into the heavens. Grandmother Spider remained with the animals and all of the people there in the four great caves of the underworld. It was left to Grandmother Spider to put things on Earth into order. So Grandmother Spider gathered all of the living creatures around her. She began to separate the people into the different Indian nations, telling them how it would be from then on for them. So it was that she made the Ute and the Zuni and the Comanche and the Pueblo people and the Hopi and all of the others. She named them and from then on they knew their names. So too she gave all of the animals their names so that they also would know who they were.

Then Grandmother Spider saw that life would not be good for the many animals and people there in the darkness of the underworld. With her two grandsons, the Hero Twins, beside her, she led the animals and the people up out of the four caverns. She led them till they came to an opening into the world above. They came out there next to the Colorado River in the place where the people still go to gather salt. As they came out, the turkey dragged his tail in the mud and his tail has been black-tipped ever since then.

Grandmother Spider sent the mourning dove ahead to find good places for the people to settle, places where there were springs and good soil for corn. Then Grandmother Spider separated the people into clans. She chose one animal to lead each of those groups of people and from then on those people carried the name of that animal. So it was that the Snake Clan and the Antelope Clan, the Mountain Lion Clan and the Deer Clan and the other clans came to be among the Hopi. The people each followed their clan animal and when they came to the place to build their homes, there they settled and there they live to this day.

The Broken Tusk

retold by Uma Krishnaswami

IN ancient times there lived a sage, a wise and gifted poet whose name was Vyasa. One day a great and beautiful story came into his mind. "I must recite it soon," he said, as his fingers counted prayer beads made from the seeds of the holy *rudraksha* tree. "I feel it in my heart. I know that the verses will flow from my lips like nectar from a flower."

There was only one problem. "I have no scribe to write this story down," said Vyasa. "The words and rhythms tremble on my tongue. If I stop to write them, the rest of the story might die inside me, and that would be a terrible thing. I must find someone who can write it down as fast as I recite, so that people who live long years from now can know this story."

Vyasa prayed to Brahma, the great god who created all things. Vyasa spent long hours in prayer. He prayed in silence and in song. He prayed in sunshine and in rain, in daylight and in darkness. He neither ate nor slept, and small ants built hills between his toes, and creeping vines began to climb up his body. In time Brahma appeared to him in a blaze of white light.

Vyasa opened his eyes, and they were bright and hot with the power of his meditation.

"Lord Brahma," said Vyasa. "I hold in my heart a story of great truth and wisdom, but I have no one to write it for me and for all the people through all time."

The unsung story seemed to hover in the air, like shimmering heat waves that dance above the rocks at summer's height. Brahma himself trembled as he felt its strength. "Ask Ganesha, the elephant-faced one," said Brahma. "He can make all obstacles disappear. He will surely help you." And Brahma vanished in his blaze of light.

Again, Vyasa prayed, this time to Ganesha. In a while, Ganesha appeared before him.

Vyasa implored, "O dancing god with the elephant head, who can hold the world in your great belly, do me the honor of being my scribe. Write down the story with which my mind overflows, so others may read it and learn from it."

"What is this story?" rumbled Ganesha.

Vyasa said, "It is the story of life and death, good and evil, war and peace."

Ganesha laughed, and his enormous belly shook. In lakes and ponds and temple tanks the pink and white lotus flowers burst into bloom and flooded the air with their magical scent. "Me?" he asked. "There are many stories in this world. No doubt yours is filled with marvels, but why ask me?"

"Lord of planets," said Vyasa, "problems and obstacles melt away when you come near. Help me."

Ganesha frowned, and the lotus blossoms closed and drooped and the clouds lowered. He laughed again, and the skies cleared. The flowers shook off water droplets and opened once more. "All right, Sage Vyasa," said Ganesha. "I'll be your scribe, but on one condition. In telling your story you must not rest or stop for any reason. If you do, I'll stop writing and go away, and the story will stay half-written."

Vyasa thought. At length he said, "You of the long trunk and lotus feet, I bow to you. But I, too, have a condition. I won't stop while I tell my story, but you must understand all that I sing, as I sing it. You must grasp every word before you write it."

"Oh, very well," said Ganesha. He laid down all the things he usually held in his four arms—goad and noose, sweet dumpling and axe. He set down the pot of sacred water from the river Ganga that nestled in the curl of his trunk. He crossed his mighty legs, adjusted the jeweled crescent moon on his forehead, and announced, "I am ready, most holy one."

Vyasa sat up straight. He cleared his throat, and began. *"Om!"* he chanted, singing the sound that is the sound of creation, the sound that the universe made when first it began. The note was deep and strong. It echoed up mountains and down valleys, until all the world knew that Vyasa had begun his story.

"Om!" chanted Vyasa, "listen. Long ago, when the ocean was milk, this story has its beginning . . ."

At the sound of Vyasa's story, the creatures of the earth grew silent and still. It was a story of cousins who loved and hated and fought each other, of power, of friends and enemies, joy and sadness. It was a story about life and everything it holds, both good and evil. For hundreds of days and hundreds of nights the story rang out. "Who hears this tale shall find with ease the path to eternal life," sang Vyasa. "Who tells it shall bestow a gift more precious than jewels."

All the time, as Vyasa chanted the verses, Ganesha wrote, fast and furious. Vyasa was careful not to pause, but as time went on he grew a little tired. So once in a while, just to give himself time to think about the next part of the story, he would throw in some difficult words or long, roundabout sentences. Ganesha, grumbling to himself, would have to stop a moment and try to understand what Vyasa had just said before writing it down. Sometimes, to make sure that Ganesha understood, Vyasa had to use many words of explanation.

Suddenly the rhythm of writing and listening, so much like the ebb and flow of the tides, was rudely interrupted by a small, sharp cracking sound.

"My pen!" muttered Ganesha.

Worn with so much use, Ganesha's pen had broken. He looked around for something else with which to carry on his writing. Only soil and grasses were all around. Ganesha took a quick look at Vyasa. The poet was taking a deep breath, getting ready to begin the next verse.

Now, Ganesha had long, elegant tusks, polished and pearly-smooth, with fine sharp tips. Reaching for his right tusk, he quickly flexed his muscles and snapped it off. Without missing a stroke, he used the broken tusk to continue writing the verse that Vyasa had already begun to recite.

It took Vyasa three years and one hundred thousand verses to complete the tale. The *devas* and *asuras* and people who lived in the three worlds all gathered to listen. The sun and moon seemed to stand still to hear it.

At length the great poem came to an end, with the last faint echoes of the very last words. Now the *devas* showered rose petals on Vyasa. Ganesha yawned carelessly, stretched, and rubbed his great belly in satisfaction. People cheered. Music echoed through the skies. Even the *asuras*, enemies of the gods, were silent in amazement.

From that time to this, Hindu children are told tales from the *Mahabharata*, the story Vyasa dictated to Ganesha. They hear it at bedtime and at play. It tells of right and wrong, duty and re- spect and loyalty. Statues of Ganesha, sculpted through many centuries, show him with a broken right tusk. He holds the bro- ken piece in one hand, so that all people who see him might re- member how Vyasa and Ganesha struck a bargain, and keep their promises to each other. As a result, one of Ganesha's names is *Ekadanta*, "One-tusk." Writers say he is their special friend and helps them when they have difficulty transforming their thoughts into words. And often in the jungle, old bull elephants who have lost a tusk remember him fondly.

CHINA

The Bridge of Magpies

told by Robert Ingpen and Barbara Hayes

SOMETIME, when you look up at the night sky, you may be lucky enough to see a silver river. This is the River of Stars that divides the northern skies from the southern kingdom of the heavens.

Long ago the King of the Land of the Stars had a beautiful daughter. This dutiful, hard-working girl sat every day at her loom weaving the clouds that floated across the skies.

One day a prince from a nearby kingdom rode near the palace of the King of the Land of the Stars. The Prince was inspecting his many horses and cattle. As he rode among the bellowing herds, the Prince looked towards the palace and saw the Princess sitting at a window, weaving. The Prince thought she was the loveliest girl he had ever seen, and asked for her hand in marriage.

The King of the Land of the Stars agreed to the match. "My hard-working daughter deserves to marry a fine Prince with many cattle," he said, "and I am even happier because the Prince lives close to me. Though she is married, I shall still be able to visit my daughter and she can continue to weave the fleecy clouds that float through my starry kingdom."

The wedding took place and the Princess went to live with the Prince in his palace. But so much for the plans of the King of the Land of the Stars! Marriage changed both the young lovers for the worse.

The Princess pushed her loom aside and wove no more clouds. She ran out into the sunshine and picked pretty flowers at the river's edge. She brushed her hair into different styles to please her husband and changed her clothes three times a day. She laughed with the dressmakers, asking for the prettiest new materials. She adorned her hands and neck with jewels.

"I have worked enough," she laughed. "Life is for enjoyment. There will be plenty of time for duty when I am old and grey."

The Prince's behavior was just as bad. He left the care of his lands and cattle to his servants. He laughed and danced with the Princess, and they spent their time idling among the flowers by the side of the river. When he was not with his wife, the

Prince rode out with wasteful, frivolous friends. He decked himself out in extravagant clothes and gambled away his money.

"Why should I have to worry about cattle and rents and harvests?" he said. "I must enjoy myself while I am still young and strong. Tomorrow may be too late."

The King of the Land of the Stars was disappointed and angry. He needed clouds for his heavens. He did not want his daughter and his son-in-law reduced to poverty and dependent upon him. He was old and he had forgotten what it was like to be young.

The king sent for his daughter and her husband. "You are not good for one another," he said. "You must be separated."

He ordered his son-in-law to be banished to the north side of the River of Stars with his servants and horses and cattle. The Princess was ordered to stay on the south side of the river with her father and to resume weaving the clouds of the heavens.

The Princess wept and the Prince pleaded, but the King of the Land of the Stars would not relent. So the lovers were parted and they spent their days in misery and bitterness.

At last, seeing his daughter's unhappiness, the King of the Land of the Stars said, "You may not be reunited with your husband, but I will allow you to go to the bank of the great River of Stars and gaze across and talk to your prodigal Prince."

The Princess ran down to the river and, looking across the shimmering stars, she saw her beloved husband and called to him. He stood on the far bank and stretched out his hands towards his beautiful wife, but still the lovers were apart.

Their unhappiness was so great that their tears fell in a flood to the earth below. Fields and houses and trees were carried away by the torrents of tears.

Finally the birds met together to decide what should be done. After much twittering and chirping, the magpies offered to fly up into the heavens and form a bridge over the River of Stars.

"If the Prince and Princess are reunited and stop their weeping, then the earth will be saved," they said.

All the magpies of the world gathered together into a whirling flock. They circled seven times around the tops of the trees, then flew up to the River of Stars. They gathered close together, head to tail, wings spread, and formed a swaying bridge from one side of the River of Stars to the other. The Prince and all his servants and horses and cattle crossed from the north to join the Princess in the southern heavens. By the time they had reached the other side, the heads of the magpies had turned black with the mud on the travelers' feet. To this day, those who look will see that the heads of magpies are black.

The Prince and Princess laughed with happiness. Their tears stopped flowing and the earth was saved. However, the King of the Land of Stars did not entirely forgive them.

"The magpies have taken pity on you," he said, "so they may continue to help you. On the seventh day of the seventh month of every year, the magpies may fly up to the heavens and make a bridge across the River of Stars. Then you may spend one day with each other. For the rest of the year you must stay apart, the Princess working at her loom and the Prince tending his estate."

So it has been through all the centuries since. As the seventh day of the seventh month draws near, the Prince and Princess move to the banks of the River of Stars. On the seventh day of the seventh month, every magpie disappears from the earth and flies up to the heavens to make the bridge over which the Prince may travel to visit the Princess.

During the rest of the year, whenever rain falls heavily from the skies, the old people of China look up and say, "The Princess is weeping with unhappiness." On the seventh day of the seventh month no rain falls because the Prince and Princess are together.

World Without Sun

retold by Neil Philip

WHEN the god Izanagi gave birth to the sun goddess Amaterasu, the moon god, Tsuki-yomi, and the god of tempests, Susanowo, he was so pleased with his offspring that he divided up the world between them. To Amaterasu he gave the rule of the High Plains of Heaven; to Tsuki-yomi he entrusted the realms of the night; and to Susanowo he gave the rule of the oceans.

But while Amaterasu and Tsuki-yomi were pleased, Susanowo screamed and howled, and complained that he did not want to rule the oceans. "I'd rather have been given charge of Yomi, the Land of Gloom," he said. But that was the province of Izanami, goddess of death and decay.

So instead of looking after the oceans, Susanowo just hung around in heaven and on earth, causing trouble wherever he went. He uprooted trees, destroyed rice paddies, and knocked down buildings. Finally he skinned a dappled pony in the heavens and dropped it through the thatched roof of the sacred weaving hall, where Amaterasu and her maidens were at work, weaving the world into pattern and order.

Amaterasu was so shocked and terrified that she fled. She shut herself inside a cave and wouldn't come out. The whole world, both heaven and earth, was plunged into darkness. Nothing would grow, and soon chaos reigned.

The gods decided that they would have to lure Amaterasu from her hiding place. They trooped to the entrance of the cave and hung a magic mirror from the branches of a tree. Then they caused roosters to crow constantly, as if it were dawn. They lit bonfires, and, while some of the gods provided music, a young goddess named Uzume climbed onto an upturned tub and began to dance. She shimmied and pranced in a way that was and so funny that all eight million gods laughed and laughed until the heavens shook.

Amaterasu was so intrigued that she opened the cave door a crack and called, "What's going on?"

"We're celebrating," replied Uzume, "because we've found a goddess who shines even more brightly than you!"

Amaterasu looked out, and the gods turned the magic mirror toward her so she saw her own reflection. As she gazed in wonder at her own radiant beauty, one of the gods seized her hand and pulled her from the cave, and another stretched a rope of straw across the entrance, saying, "This is as far back as you may go."

So Amaterasu was tricked back into the world by the laughter of the gods and the beauty of her own reflection, and since that time the sun has never again failed.

As for Susanowo, the gods punished him for his part in the affair by cutting off his beard and his fingernails and his toenails, and they banished him from the High Plains of Heaven. But he and his powerful storms are still causing mischief on earth.

USA (HAWAII)
Hiiaka

retold by Robert D. San Souci

Hiiaka is the beautiful youngest sister and favorite of Pele, the great fire goddess who lives in the molten heart of Hawaii's Kilauea Volcano. Pele rules over a family of fire gods, including Hiiaka and their brother, Lono-makua. While Pele is easily angered and quick to punish offenders with fiery eruptions of lava, Hiiaka is calm and kind and always ready to help humanity. Though she can be fierce when battling the dragon-like *mo'o* monsters, Hiiaka's greatest gifts are creative: she is a healer and the one who taught the people of Hawaii the arts of the hula, lei-making, and composing the long chants that are some of the finest examples of Hawaii's oral folklore tradition.

ONE day Hawaii's powerful fire goddess, Pele, sent for her sister, Hiiaka, who was wandering amid groves of scarlet-blossomed *'ohi'a* trees, far from the barren black lava fields and blazing fire pits of her home. The young goddess returned to Kilauea Volcano at once and sought her sister, Pele, who commanded her, "Find my beloved Lohiau, who has been stolen away by evil spirits."

Now Hiiaka knew that what her sister was asking involved great danger. But she knew how much her sister loved the mortal, who was chief of a distant island; and she had a great affection for Pele, who had always shown her special favor. So she said, "You are my dearest sister and truest friend. I will find Lohiau and scorn the perils of the journey."

But Hiiaka's loyal and courageous words hid the uneasiness she felt. She, too, had looked upon Lohiau with loving eyes. Because he was promised to Pele, she had denied her longing. But thoughts of him came often to her. So she had vowed to do everything in her power to keep apart from him. Now, commanded to go to his aid, she feared that the greatest danger lay not on the path ahead, but in her own heart.

Pele sensed nothing of Hiiaka's disquiet. To aid her sister on her quest, she gifted Hiiaka with a magical *pa-u,* a skirt that held the power of lightning in its folds. She traveled with Pau-o-palae (whose name means "skirt of palai fern"), her *kahu,* guardian servant. The goddess of ferns, Pau-o-palae provided Hiiaka with a beautiful robe woven of ferns.

Together they set out on their great adventure. Their route took them beyond a beach of black lava sands into a dense forest, where they met Pana-ewa, a witch-*mo'o* in the form of a huge reptile. The evil creature could take many forms. Alerted by her brothers who were little birds, the monster blocked Hiiaka's path.

"Why have you brought me no *awa* to drink, no *taro* and red fish to eat, no *tapas* for mats?" she challenged. "Had you brought such gifts, I would not bar your way."

"Pana-ewa, stand aside!" commanded Hiiaka.

"There is no way for you to pass," hissed Pana-ewa. "I will kill you. I will swallow you."

Then she laughed and called up fog and rain and wind to drive Hiiaka back. From the depths of the jungle, the *mo'o* summoned forth *eepas*, gnomelike beings, and many other vicious forest creatures to torment the travelers. Finally, tiring of the game, Pana-ewa herself attacked the goddess in her fog-body, choking her with tentacles of chill mist. But Hiiaka shook her magic skirt, threw the demon back with lightning bolts, and scattered the mist.

Next Pana-ewa took the form of freezing rain, then of a mighty wind that hurled trees at Hiiaka. But the goddess used the power of her lightning skirt to shatter the trunks and drive the monster back again. Pana-ewa fled deep into the forest, while Hiiaka took the opportunity to rest and regain her strength.

But the wicked one sent all sorts of horrible creatures against her. they ambushed Hiiaka at every turn and took a multitude of disguises. A withered bush, a bunch of grass, a moss-grown stone—any of these might suddenly spit venom or tear at the goddess with hook and claw. She drove them all away with the power of her bamboo knife and lightning skirt. Beside her, Pau-o-palae fought just as bravely.

Soon both were nearly dead from wounds and weariness—so tired that they could barely move. With her last breath, Hiiaka called for her sister, Pele, to help.

Her cry rolled like thunder across mountain and valley and stream to reach Pele, ever watchful in her fiery lake.

Angered, Pele sent a lightning storm that burned up Hiiaka's enemies in the forest. Then rain came in torrents, flooding the valleys with red water, sweeping Pana-ewa and her cohorts out to sea, where they were devoured by sharks.

Hiiaka's journey next took her to a lovely place of cloud-capped mountains and flowing rivers. There the goddesses of lightning and ferns met the human Wahine-omao, whose name means the "light-colored woman." Awed to be in the presence of such a powerful figure as Hiiaka, the woman threw herself on the ground before the goddess. But Hiiaka saw that she was a person with an honest, generous heart, as well as brave and beautiful. So she invited her to join in the quest.

The three—the two goddesses and Wahine-omao—swam across to the island called Hilo. At a hut on a bluff overlooking the shore, two girls—sisters—offered them dried fish and a little calabash full of *poi* porridge. Quickly, the three visitors sensed that the girls were distressed about something.

"What troubles you so?" asked Hiiaka.

"We are fearful for our father," said the first girl.

Her sister continued, "He took his canoe out last night, and he has not returned."

Hiiaka walked to the edge of the cliff. She looked first far out to sea, then down to where the waves crashed on the shore below. There she discovered the spirit of the girls' father wandering the shore.

Warning the others that they must not shed a single tear, Hiiaka climbed down the cliff face and attempted to capture the wandering spirit. She planned to force it back into the body of the fisherman, which lay on the shore where the sea had washed it up.

But the ghost tried to elude her. "Let me go," the spirit pleaded. "I will have a brighter and happier life among the trees and ferns of the forest."

Finally, Hiiaka used her "strong hand of Kilauea"—the power that belonged to her as one of the divine family living in the fire pit of Kilauea Volcano—to catch the spirit. Hiiaka also had vast powers of healing. Now she poured fresh water from a nearby stream over the body, while she chanted:

> Here is the water of life.
> *E ala e!* Awake! Arise!
> Let life return.
> The power of death is over.
> It is lifted,
> It has flown away.

At last, the ghost was compelled to reenter the body through its eyes and nose. Breath returned, the body stirred; the fisherman lived again.

The goddess and her companions continued their search,

which grew ever more dangerous.

She had to fight Mo'o-lau, the dragon, who had enslaved the people who lived along the coast of yet another island. The dragon boasted, "You have no path through my lands unless you have great strength."

Hiiaka accepted his challenge. She fought with the power of her lightning *pa-u*, while he struck at her with his swift-moving tail and tried to grab her with his mighty jaws. Both had powerful magic to call upon, and again and again they fought each other to a standstill. But, at last, the goddess prevailed. She destroyed Mo'o-lau and the lesser dragons who had rallied to the monster's call for help.

Pau-o-palae, the goddess of ferns, met the chief of the people who had been enslaved by the dragons but were now free. They fell in love and were married. Then Pau-o-palae remained with her husband, while Hiiaka and Wahine-omao continued their search for Lohiau.

Hiiaka also had to drive away Mahiki, the whirlwind, and slay Makakiu, the sea serpent, before she finally crossed the sea in an outrigger canoe to the island, Maui, where Lohiau was kept in a mountain cave guarded by dragon women, enemies of Pele. These creatures raised a terrible storm, wrapped the mountains in freezing, clinging fog, and sent down avalanches of rock.

But Hiiaka fought past all these dangers. The final battle took place in a forested valley in front of the cave. There, at first, the goddess was almost defeated because the dragon women seemed able to survive the terrible power of her lightning. But again she used her magical "strong hand of Kilauea." This time, she caused the very trees and plants to come alive, twisting and twining roots and branches and vines around the dragon women. Then Hiiaka caused the hapless creatures to be hurled down the cliffs, where their bodies were broken into pieces on the rocks below.

At that instant, the storm quieted and the fog lifted. Then Hiiaka called forth Lohiau from the cave. She embraced him as a brother and began making preparations for the long journey home. Though the fire of love in her heart threatened to consume her, she resolved to keep the secret from Lohiau and remain loyal to Pele.

But Pele, in the fire pit of Kilauea, had first grown impatient, then furious as the days had passed without Hiiaka bringing Lohiau back to her.

"Where is my sister? Why has she not returned?" demanded the jealous goddess. As her anger grew, she cried out, "It must be that my faithless sister and Lohiau have fallen in love. They have forgotten me!"

Indeed, the young man *had* become charmed by Hiiaka, yet the girl remained faithful to Pele. But before she could escort Lohiau back to Kilauea, an enraged Pele caused the volcano to erupt. She stamped the floor of the fire pit so hard that the crater convulsed and the land trembled for miles around. Finally, she loosed a seething, bubbling, hissing flood of lava to burn up the land and all living things. The sky turned red as her anger turned into fire clouds—boiling fountains of flame and cinder—that shot up to the very curve of heaven; and the air was filled with the explosions of flaming gas called "Pele's curses"; and hot stones fell like rain on the tortured earth.

Fearful, Hiiaka hid herself and her companions on a small island. Then she sent Wahine-omao to Pele to act as messenger and calm her sister's anger. But the fire goddess imprisoned the unhappy woman in a cave and would not listen to her story.

Then Pele summoned her brother, Lono-makua, who has charge over the earth fires. She commanded him, "Go. Find the unfaithful couple. Kindle volcanoes around them and burn them to ashes."

Lono-makua did as he was commanded. Fountains of fire burst from the earth and ringed Hiiaka and Lohiau on their tiny island refuge. Although the terrible heat and flames could not hurt Hiiaka, the fire streams of lave instantly turned Lohiau to a shrunken figure of stone, and his spirit fled to a cool forest on a distant mountain.

Hiiaka, devastated by the death of Lohiau and the betrayal by her sister, became crazed with sorrow and anger. She began to hurl lightning bolts at the walls of Kilauea. She planned to break down the sides of the crater, so that the sea might pour through into the fire pit.

Then Pele realized that Hiiaka intended to fill the pit with water, so that her fires would be imprisoned and drowned. Pele's home would be destroyed, just as the monster Kama-puaa had once ruined Ka-lua-Pele (The Pit of Pele), her former home, with torrents of rain. Fearing that she would again be driven from her dwelling place, Pele looked for a way to turn aside her sister's wrath.

She released Wahine-omao from her prison and listened to her story. Then, filled with regret, she sent the human back to Hiiaka to calm her.

This Wahine-omao did, gently reminding Hiiaka, "Surely you can return Lohiau's ghost to his body, as you once returned the spirit of the drowned fisherman."

Indeed, this is what happened. Hiiaka repeated the ceremonies and prayers and called back her beloved's spirit from the distant forest. Upon the lifeless, stone form of Lohiau, she poured out water from a calabash, crying,

> Here's water, the Water of Life!
> Grant life in abundance, life!
> I pray thee awake!
> Here am I, Hiiaka.
> Awake, I beg and entreat thee!
> Let my prayer speed its way!

With a cry of joy, she saw the cold and withered form gain fullness, warmth, and color. There was a sudden rush of air into Lohiau's lungs; his eyelids flickered; he sat up. Gently Hiiaka and Wahine-omao led him to the ocean shore. There all three performed the ritual washing that removed the uncleanness of death. And when they emerged from the sunlit waves, each seemed to glow with a fresh and radiant beauty.

At last Pele and Hiiaka were reconciled. Pele realized that her sister was deeply in love with Lohiau—yet would never betray her. And she saw with sorrow, now, instead of anger, that Lohiau's eyes burned with love for Hiiaka. So Pele put aside her claim on the man, and Hiiaka and Lohiau were wed. And Wahine-omao became the wife of Lono-makua. But Hiiaka found that her adventures and her love for Lohiau had forever changed her. She could not take her former place in Pele's service at Kilauea.

She set sail for the island of Kauai, the land that Lohiau claimed as his own. There she was eventually joined by her faithful attendants, Pau-o-palae and Wahine-omao, their husbands, and certain of her sisters.

Many other adventures lay in wait for the brave and much-beloved goddess whom the islander people still refer to in song as *Hiiaka—ka no'iau—i ka poli o Pele*, "Hiiaka, the wise, the darling of Pele."

But those tales are for another telling.

Krishna and the Serpent

retold by John Bailey

VISHNU the preserver, lord of the universe, took the form of a little boy called Krishna, so that he could fight against the evil in the world. Krishna was dark-skinned and handsome, and was the ring-leader in all the mischievous games the village children played. His mother and the other women laughed at his pranks; Krishna was everyone's favorite.

When he was seven, Krishna and his half-brother Rama used to go with the cowherds and help look after the cattle. All day long they played in the fields and woods where the cattle grazed, making garlands of leaves and flowers and running in and out of the trees. Krishna was musical, and he often sat down and played enchanting tunes on a flute he had made. The other children and the cowherds sat at his feet, and even the cows, and the birds and animals of the forest, came closer to listen to the magical sounds.

The cowherds usually took their cattle to the banks of the river Kalindi to quench their thirst. But one day all the cows that drank from the river fell ill and died. The evil serpent-king Kaliya had entered the river, and his presence poisoned the water.

Soon nothing could live in or near the river. The fish died; birds flying over the water were scorched and burned; even the crocodiles left the riverbanks and crashed through the forest in search of fresh water.

No one knew what to do. Everyone was afraid. At last Krishna decided that the time had come for him to find the serpent in its lair and kill it. He set off alone, and went upriver till he came to a deep pool where the water foamed and boiled, and the trees were dead along the banks—Kaliya's lair.

"It was to overcome the wicked that I came into the world in human form," Krishna thought. "For the sake of my people now, I must dive into the serpent's home and kill him."

He climbed a dead tree on the riverbank, edged out along a branch, and dived into the water.

Kaliya was furious at being disturbed by a little human boy, and rushed at Krishna to kill him. Krishna wriggled out of reach and swam to the surface to breathe. Kaliya followed him, trying to seize him in his coils and drag him down into the depths. Soon the water was seething with the serpent's poison and the writhing of its body. Krishna seized its head and climbed onto it, carefully keeping clear of the flickering, poisonous fangs.

Angrily, Kaliya tried to shake him off. Krishna hung on for his life. The water roared and churned round him; the snake wriggled and plunged; there was a ringing in his ears as the poison entered him from the water and slowly took effect. The world went dark.

By now, some of the cowherds had missed Krishna, and followed him upriver. They arrived just in time to see Kaliya dragging the boy's unconscious body down into the swirling depths. Horrified, they ran to fetch Rama and the other villagers.

Soon hundreds of frightened people lined the banks. They peered down into the murky depths. In the slime and mud of the river-bottom, Krishna lay still and silent in Kaliya's coils. The people cried out and wrung their hands in grief; many of them loved him so dearly they were ready to jump into the poisonous waters to try and save his life.

But Rama held them back. He was Krishna's half-brother, and knew of his divine nature. He looked down into the dark water, and called out in a loud voice: "Krishna, great lord of all the gods, have you forgotten who you are? You are Vishnu the preserver, lord of the universe. It was to overcome evil that you became Krishna. Don't give way to human weakness; use a god's power, and crush the serpent!"

At the bottom of the river, Krishna heard; he opened his eyes and smiled. Using a god's power, he flexed his body to break the serpent's grip, then sprang free. He jumped onto the monster's head, and began to dance. All his music, all his godlike skill, poured out in a dance of death on Kaliya's head. Gradually, Kaliya was forced to submit. He stopped struggling, and at last lay dazed and still.

Now Kaliya's wives, the serpent queens, saw that their king was beaten. They came out of hiding, and begged Krishna to spare his life. "We did not recognize you, lord of the gods," they cried. "Now we see you are Vishnu, lord of all. Be merciful. His poison is spent. Spare his life, and let him go."

The little boy Krishna swam to the bank, and looked down at the beaten monster.

"I created you, Kaliya, and now I will spare your life," he said. "Go now, with all your wives. Never again enter the waters of the river Kalindi. Your home is the ocean; stay there, and harm no mortal man again."

So, with his wives and followers, Kaliya the serpent-king left the river Kalindi and swam to the ocean. The river waters became clear and pure again. The villagers cheered and praised the little boy who was also their lord and god.

Coyote and the Blackbirds

told by Nancy Van Laan

COYOTE was walking along, *loppa loppa lop, loppa loppa lop,* feeling pleased and proud of himself as usual.

Just then, he heard: *KEOW! KEOW! Flutter, flutter, flap!*

Coyote stopped.

He looked up. Blackbirds!

Flitta-flitting here, *flitta-flitting* there, the blackbirds were chattering excitedly.

Coyote cocked his head and listened.

"*KEOW! KEOW!* It's going to hail! It's going to hail!" they called.

Coyote moved closer.

"Bring me my bag! Bring me my bag!" said one.

"It's going to hail! It's going to hail!" called another.

Coyote looked at the sky. It was a clear, deep blue.

"What are you talking about?" asked Coyote.

"Too busy to talk, too busy to talk," they chattered.

"What is wrong with all of you?" asked Coyote.

"Just you wait, just you wait," they said.

Coyote sat down. He yawned. He watched. He waited. He yawned again.

As the blackbirds sang, "*KEOW! KEOW!*" they hung buckskin bags from the branches of the tallest tree.

All this fuss made Coyote nervous. He began to pace back and forth, back and forth, *lop loppa loppa lop, lop loppa loppa lop.*

"Maybe these blackbirds know something I don't," thought Coyote.

Loppa loppa lop. Loppa loppa lop.

"Maybe there's a good reason why they are hanging bags in the trees."

Loppa loppa lop. Loppa loppa lop.

Coyote stood on his hind legs and called out: "*HA-HAY-OOO!* Whatever it is that you are doing, I want to do, too!"

Coyote hated to be left out of anything.

The blackbirds seemed pleased.

"Oh, friend Coyote," they called sweetly, "we would love for you to join us."

"Good!" said Coyote, feeling much better now. "Tell me," he said, "what exactly are you doing with those bags?"

"Oh, friend Coyote," said the blackbirds, "we shall hide inside them. When it hails, we won't be pelted to death."

"What a good idea!" said Coyote. "May I join you?"

"Oh, yes! Oh, yes!" chirped the blackbirds. "Good idea! Good idea!"

Quickly, Coyote ran home, found a large bag just his size, and brought it back to the blackbirds, who were waiting.

"Just right! Just right!" called the blackbirds, trying hard not to laugh.

"Get in, get in!" they said.

Coyote climbed inside the bag. The blackbirds flew down.

"Tie the rope! Tie the rope!" said one.

"Pull it up! Pull it up!" said another.

Soon Coyote, inside the bag, was pulled high above the ground, where he swung back and forth, back and forth, from the branch of the tallest tree.

The blackbirds, full of mischief, gathered pebbles from the ground.

"KEOW! KEOW!" they called excitedly. "Here comes the storm! Here comes the hail!" Then they threw stones at the swinging bag as hard as they could.

"Mercy, oh, mercy!" yelled Coyote. "What a terrible storm it is indeed!"

"KEE-KEEOW!" chirped the blackbirds as they pelted Coyote.

"Ouch!" said Coyote. "Thank goodness I'm safe inside this bag!"

"KAYAI! KAYAI!" cried the blackbirds, pretending to suffer as they threw pebbles at the bag.

"OW! OW!" howled Coyote. "If it hurts me like this, it must really hurt you!"

"Yes, yes!" cried the blackbirds. "It hurts us much more than it hurts you, friend Coyote." Then they pelted the bag again, even harder this time.

"OUCH!" yelled Coyote. "That one nearly hit my eye!"

"Be brave, be brave, friend Coyote," crooned the blackbirds. "You are much stronger than we are." They pelted him as hard as they could.

"OW! OW! OWOOOOO!" yelled Coyote.

The blackbirds were too tired to throw anymore. They untied the rope and slowly, slowly let the bag down to the ground. As soon as the bag opened up, they rushed to the top of the tree.

"Ohhh . . ." groaned Coyote, crawling out, so bruised and sore he could barely move. "I think I am dead," he said.

Coyote lay quite still for a while, then opened his eyes and looked around.

What? The sun was shining!

What? There were no clouds in the sky!

What? The ground was dry! There were no hailstones anywhere!

"AUGH! AUGHHH! What a mean trick you have played on me!" Coyote groaned as the blackbirds, laughing and cackling, flew over his head, just out of reach.

Coyote limped home in a terrible rage as the blackbirds followed, teasing and taunting him.

"AUGH! I'll eat you all!" he growled.

"You can't catch us! You can't catch us!" they screamed.

But the next day, he did.

And from that time forth, blackbird stew became Coyote's favorite dinner.

This is how war on this earth first began.

Is that so? Yes, that is so.

Head Over Heart

Or, How Monkey Tricked Shark And So Saved His Life

retold by Martin Bennett

ONCE upon a story, a million moons ago, there was a monkey. Now, there can be no monkey without a tree. And so there was a tree. And the tree of this monkey happened to be by the sea—not for the sake of the rhyme only, but because that was where it was.

Now, this tree was full of mangoes and more mangoes, enough to feed a herd of elephants if there had been one nearby. Which there wasn't. The monkey never had to go to the farm or the market or the supermarket. Instead, he would play all day amidst the tree's branches. Then, when he got tired, he would sit down on his favorite branch to rest, and pick some mangoes, fresh as fresh could be. Sometimes he did this because he was hungry. Sometimes he did it for the not-very-particular reason that he liked throwing mangoes into the sea below and watching the splash they made. It was so pretty, the way the ripples spread out one after the other across the still, blue water, the sun flashing dancingly between.

A shark, who had made a habit of basking and swimming nearby, liked it too. Every time a fresh uneaten mango fell into the water, the shark would eat it. Mmmmmm! Mangoes made such a delicious diet after eating fish all the time, fish and more fish and the occasional jellyfish for dessert.

Every day Monkey would amuse himself by throwing mangoes into the sea and watching the ripples. It was just as entertaining as watching television. So, every day, the sea his playground, the shark would amuse himself by pointing his nose above the water and catching the mangoes between his teeth. He did not bother to spit out the stones. What is the stone of a mango to a shark who can swallow a man, bones and everything? Yes, even a monkey if necessary . . . But for now, at least, mangoes and more mangoes were enough. Monkey plucked and threw them. Shark caught and ate them. It was a nice arrangement. Despite belonging to different elements, soon Monkey and Shark had become friends.

Now, friends the world over respect the saying: "One good

turn deserves another." Soon Shark decided, in his own shark-ish way, that it was time to pay Monkey back for his kindness.

"Mister Monkey, your mangoes are so sweet," barked Shark, opening his jaws above the water. "Look, it's high time I repaid you. Why not jump down from your tree and I can take you to my people? Then you will see what sharkish hospitality is really like."

"But what about my fur?" replied Monkey. "You know we mon-keys do not like getting our fur wet. No, the sea is fine for throw-ing mangoes into and watching the splash they make, but as for swimming in, that is another thing completely." Monkey looked into Shark's jaws, less happy about accepting his friend's offer than his friend was in giving it.

"No problem," said Shark, surfacing above the water once more. "You don't have to get wet at all. All you have to do is jump onto my back and hold on to my fin. I will swim close to the surface of the water, don't worry. I promise you a waterproof ride all the way. So you are coming, I hope. You know, I hate to take no as an answer."

"Well, all right," agreed Monkey, for want of a better reply.

Monkey jumped down from his tree. Soon he was on the sea-shore, hopping this way and that to avoid the oncoming waves. Shark steered his body close and Monkey climbed dryly on to his back.

"Ready? Hold on tight!" And with a flick of Shark's tail, off they went into the Bight of Benin, for that was what this part of the ocean was named. Shark swam; Monkey sat, holding on tightly to Shark's fin to balance better. The waves whizzed by and Mon-key looked back to see his tree getting smaller and smaller till it was out of sight completely. Already they were in mid-ocean; water, water everywhere, tilting this way and that.

"Is it . . . er . . . is it far?" inquired Monkey weakly. He was be-ginning to suffer from worry and seasickness combined. Worse still, he remembered the old sailors' song: "The Bight of Benin, O the Bight of Benin! Few come out though many go in!" and could not get it out of his head.

"No, not far at all," Shark assured Monkey through his teeth. "Only, Monkey, there is just one thing I should tell you. You know what a good friend you are to me, and I would not tell you other-wise. It's just that our chief—Chief Sarkin Shark III, Ruler of the Bight of Benin and Anti-Protector of the Guinea Coast—is dying from a strange illness. We have given him codliver oil, crushed seahorses, squid's ink, boiled anemones, but all to no effect. There is only one thing left that might cure him . . ."

"And what is that?" asked Monkey, gripping Shark's fin still tighter.

"A monkey's heart. Chief Sarkin must eat a monkey's heart. It's the only medicine. Now I'm sure you wouldn't mind providing us with your own?"

"I would be only too happy to help. Only . . . only, you see, Mister Shark, how can I donate my heart to your chief when I haven't brought it with me?"

"Haven't brought it with you? But how?" exclaimed Shark.

"So you have not heard that we monkeys leave our hearts hanging up where we sleep. It may sound a bit unscientific, but don't ask me why, except it's an ancient custom among us. You see, we only use our hearts at night. Now, if you had told me earlier about your chief's illness, I could have arranged to bring my heart with me. What a pity!"

Shark ground his teeth and groaned.

"It's true. I would even cross my heart if I had it with me! Of course, you can go ahead and kill me if you like," offered Monkey. "But imagine what will happen when your people open me up afterwards and find there is no heart inside me? What will the other sharks think of you then? I would hate to see you embarrassed before your chief, especially considering his critical condition. I am only telling you this as a special friend, you understand . . ."

"Oh, what shall I do? What shall I do?" wailed Shark. (Being one of them himself, he knew how merciless his tribe could be.)

"We will just have to swim back to land. There is nothing else for it," concluded Monkey. "Then I can go and fetch my heart down from where it is hanging. Don't worry, it won't take long."

Following his passenger's advice, Shark did a U-turn there in mid-ocean. Countless waves later, there was Monkey's beloved mango tree rising above the seashore. The fruit dangled down in fat green clusters and the sun caught in the branches like a many-colored ribbon.

Shark swam closer to shore and when his stomach was flat against the sand, Monkey dismounted from his back.

"Don't worry, Mister Shark. I will go and come back just as soon as I can fetch my heart from its hanging-place," assured Monkey. Then he scampered across the white sand to his home sweet home. Meanwhile, Shark was left to swim round and round in vicious circles, waiting for Monkey to bring his heart as promised. But Monkey's cheerful "go-and-come-back" was definitely more a matter of "go" than "come back." If Shark had

had legs, you can be sure he would have used them as quickly as you can snap your teeth. As it was, he had only a fin and a tail, as useless on dry land as Monkey's fur was useless in water.

One hour later Shark was still swimming around. His tail was aching, his stomach was growling, and his head was getting dizzier and dizzier. Worse still, if Monkey did not come soon, they would miss the outgoing tide. Shark thought of Chief Sarkin Shark III, Ruler of the Bight of Benin and Anti-Protector of the Guinea Coast, of whether he was dead yet or not, of what punishment he (Shark) might expect on his return.

"Look here, Monkey! How much longer are you going to keep me waiting? Don't you realize our chief may die at any moment? Can you find your heart or not?"

"So you think I am a fool?!?" Monkey's voice echoed down from the safety of his tree. (Recovered from his seasickness, he was merrily eating mangoes.) "You think I've not seen through your sharkish tricks?!? No, Mister Shark. You can carry on swimming round till your tail drops off for all I care. I am not coming. Not for all the salt in the ocean. Just leave me to eat my mangoes. And as for my heart, it is in the right place. It's not hanging anywhere, but is here beneath my chest just as it should be. So you think I can give it away so easily? Never, not even to a girlfriend, let alone to a shark like you. No, I am not stupid. No monkey's heart for you. From now on, no mangoes, either."

And so Shark, heartless creature that he was, had no choice but to swim back towards the center of the ocean. What happened on his return—whether he was punished or not—has been washed away by the tides of time. Not that Monkey in his tree cared a groundnut one way or the other. Or a mango. By the skin of Shark's teeth he had learned his lesson.

And that is why, kind listeners, you will never see a monkey bathing in the sea.

Nor, for that matter, will you find a shark eating mangoes.

The Deceitful Pelican

told by Robert Ingpen and Barbara Hayes

THE river tumbled from the mountains and slid over the edge
of the rocks into a deep pool. The noise and turmoil made by
the falling water was endless, or so Ruan the fish believed.
Ruan did as his father had done before him, and as his grandfather had done before that, and as his great-grandfather had
done before that. Ruan could think no further back than the
days of his great-grandfather. He was not clever. Few fish are.

When he was not eating Ruan lay in the cool water at the
bottom of the pool and tried to look like a mottled brown stone.
His father had told him to behave so. His grandfather had told
his father to behave so, and his great-grandfather had told his
grandfather to behave so. None of them had ever wanted to do
anything different. Fish are like that.

One morning a pelican came to stand by the side of the pool.
The great pouch under his large beak was empty. For days the
pelican had had little luck with his hunting; he was tired and
hungry. He stared down into the pool and saw Ruan the fish
lying on the bottom, pretending to be a mottled brown stone.
The pelican was a solitary creature and liked to stand by himself and think. That day he was thinking up a cunning plot.

The pelican tossed his head and said, "The creatures of this
pool live in times of dreadful danger. How I admire their courage."

At once Ruan the fish hurried up from the bottom of the pool,
filled with curiosity. He forgot everything his father and grandfather and great-grandfather had said about pretending to be a
mottled brown stone. Fish have few brains.

"Dear me! Dear me! What is this talk of danger?" he flapped.
"I have a young family to consider. Tell me what is wrong?"

The pelican looked down at Ruan with interest. "You have a
young family?" he asked. "Tender little fishlets are they?"

"Oh, indeed, indeed!" agreed Ruan the fish. "I have many
sweet babies. Tell me what danger threatens."

"There is going to be a terrible drought," said the pelican. "Soon
no more water will flow from the mountains. The waterfall will
cease to tumble and this pool will dry up to nothing. Then, I am
sorry to have to tell you, you and your young ones will die."

Ruan the fish was alarmed at this news. He did not stop to think that the waterfall was tumbling as strongly and as noisily as it ever had. He did not consider that, if indeed there had been a drought, the flow of water would already be slowing.

No, he swam in circles and wailed, "What will become of my dear children? What will become of my loving wife? What will become of me?"

"How can I ignore the cries of such a dutiful parent!" sighed the pelican. "I will help you, if you wish."

"Can you? Will you? I will always be grateful to you," puffed Ruan the fish.

"I have traveled the world," said the pelican. "I know many things. I know the way to a pool that is fed by a deep spring. In the worst drought that pool never runs dry. I will carry you and your family to this place of safety. You can see that my beak is large and comfortable. Will you snuggle into it and make the journey?"

"Oh, indeed, indeed we will!" gasped Ruan. "A friend such as you is beyond price."

"I will take you first to show you the beauty of your new home," said the pelican and, opening his mouth, he waited for Ruan the fish to jump in.

Eagerly Ruan flipped his tail and leaped out of the water. His head spun as he swayed to and fro in the suffocating darkness of the pelican's beak.

The pelican walked a few paces round a corner of the hillside to a pool farther down the same river. It could have been a journey of a hundred miles for all Ruan knew in his flurry of excitement.

FLOP! The pelican opened its mouth and let Ruan slide into the cool water.

"Wonderful!" gasped the fish, when he had recovered his senses. "You have found a new home of exquisite beauty for me and my wife and little ones. Please take me back to them, so that I can prepare them for their removal."

Once more the pelican opened his beak and then carried Ruan the fish the few paces to his old home.

"Hurry! Hurry! Prepare for a long journey," called Ruan, twisting through the water and calling his family away from where they were safely feeding. "Soon this pool will dry up. Our lives are in terrible danger, but a wonderful new friend will carry us to a beautiful new home."

His wife and young ones were confused at this startling news, but after a while they gathered their wits together and swam up to the edge of the water.

129

"I will go first and wait for you in the new pool," said Ruan.

"Of course! Of course!" replied his wife and children. "Look out for the best feeding places. Find where the shadows fall so that we can keep out of the sun."

They had never been so excited before. The pelican bent down and, catching Ruan in his beak, carried him to the pool around the corner of the hillside.

Ruan didn't see the pelican again. He looked for good places to feed and found where the shadows fell across the new pool. He waited at the edge of the water for his family to join him, but he was disappointed. No one came.

He flapped anxiously from side to side, asking the fish in the new pool if they had seen any youngsters arriving. They had not, nor had they heard talk of any drought. Ruan began to have the most terrible doubts.

Meanwhile, the pelican was taking Ruan's little ones, one by one, from the old pool under the waterfall. Instead of carrying them to the new pool, the pelican was swallowing them into his pouch.

"Who is next?" called the pelican each time he returned to the waterside.

"Me! Me! Take me next!" called the baby fish, pressing eagerly forward and showing that they were true children of their father.

When all the fish were in his pouch, the pelican turned his eyes towards the crabs, who lived in the same pool by the waterfall. He told them the same story about the drought and how the pool would soon be dry.

"Really! How very interesting!" said the oldest and biggest crab. "Bend down and tell me more."

Now crabs are quite different from fish. They can walk from the water to the land and back again. They travel the world and they see things and they learn from what they see. The oldest and biggest crab had already concluded that if the water was still pouring over the waterfall as strongly as ever it had, then the story of the drought could not be true. He had also decided that the pelican was a creature that the inhabitants of the pool could well manage without.

The pelican bent down to tell the crab about the wonderful pool fed by the ever-flowing spring to which he could carry him. Before the pelican could utter any more of his lies, the crab seized him round the throat and squeezed with his pincers until the pelican was dead. The bird's beak fell open and all the little fish and their mother swam out to safety in their old pool.

The only person to suffer any harm from the whole affair was the pelican himself. Even silly Ruan had the sense to swim out of his new pool and back up the river to his old pool. There he was reunited with his family and went back to pretending he was a mottled brown stone.

The Famine

from *The Song of Hiawatha*

by Henry Wadsworth Longfellow

O THE long and dreary Winter!
O the cold and cruel Winter!
Ever thicker, thicker, thicker
Froze the ice on lake and river,
Ever deeper, deeper, deeper
Fell the snow o'er all the landscape,
Fell the covering snow and drifted
Through the forest, round the village.
　　Hardly from his buried wigwam
Could the hunter force a passage;
With his mittens and his snow-shoes
Vainly he walked he through the forest,
Sought for bird or beast and found none.
Saw no track of deer or rabbit,
In the snow beheld no footprints,
In the ghastly, gleaming forest
Fell, and could not rise from weakness,
Perished there from cold and hunger.
　　O the famine and the fever!
O the wasting of the famine!
O the blasting of the fever!
O the wailing of the children!
O the anguish of the women!
　　All the earth was sick and famished,
Hungry was the air around them,
Hungry was the sky above them,
And the hungry stars in heaven
Like the eyes of wolves glared at them!
　　Into Hiawatha's wigwam
Came two other guests, as silent
As ghosts were, and as gloomy,
Waited not to be invited,
Did not parley at the doorway,
Sat there without word of welcome
In the seat of Laughing Water;

Looked with haggard eyes and hollow
At the face of Laughing Water.
    And the foremost said: "Behold me!
I am Famine, Buckadawin!"
And the other said: "Behold me!
I am Fever, Ahkosewin!"
    And the lovely Minnehaha
Shuddered as they looked upon her,
Shuddered at the words they uttered,
Lay down on her bed in silence,
Hid her face, but made no answer;
Lay there trembling, freezing, burning
At the looks they cast upon her,
At the fearful words they uttered.
    Forth into the empty forest
Rushed the maddened Hiawatha;
In his heart was deadly sorrow,
In his face a stony firmness;
On his brow the sweat of anguish
Started, but it froze, and fell not.
    Wrapped in furs, and armed for hunting,
With his mighty bow of ash-tree,
With his quiver full of arrows,
With his mittens, Minjekahwun,
Into the vast and vacant forest
On his snow-shoes strode he forward.
    "Gitche Manito, the Mighty!"
Cried he with his face uplifted
In that bitter hour of anguish,
"Give your children food, O father!
Give us food, or we must perish!
Give us food for Minnehaha,
For my dying Minnehaha!"
    Through the far-resounding forest,
Through the forest vast and vacant,
Rang that cry of desolation,
But there came no other answer
Than the echo of the woodlands,
"Minnehaha! Minnehaha!"
    All day long roved Hiawatha
In that melancholy forest,
Through the shadow of whose thickets,
In the pleasant days of Summer,

Of that ne'er-forgotten Summer,
He had brought his young wife homeward
From the land of the Dacotahs;
When the birds sang in the thickets,
And the streamlets laughed and glistened,
And the air was full of fragrance,
And the lovely Laughing Water
Said, with voice that did not tremble,
"I will follow you, my husband!"
　　In the wigwam with Nokomis,
With those gloomy guests that watched her,
With the Famine and the Fever,
She was lying, the Beloved,
She the dying Minnehaha.
　　"Hark!" she said, "I hear a rushing,
Hear a roaring and a rushing,
Hear the Falls of Minnehaha
Calling to me from a distance!"
"No, my child!" said old Nokomis,
"'Tis the night-wind in the pine-trees!"
"Look!" she said, "I see my father
Standing lonely at his doorway,
Beckoning to me from his wigwam,
In the land of the Dacotahs!"
"No, my child!" said old Nokomis,
"'Tis the smoke that waves and beckons!"
　　"Ah!" said she, "the eyes of Pauguk
Glare upon me in the darkness;
I can feel his icy fingers
Clasping mine amid the darkness!
Hiawatha! Hiawatha!"
　　And the desolate Hiawatha,
Far away amid the forest,
Miles away among the mountains,
Heard that sudden cry of anguish,
Heard the voice of Minnehaha
Calling to him in the darkness,
"Hiawatha! Hiawatha!"
　　Over snow-fields waste and pathless,
Under snow-encumbered branches,
Homeward hurried Hiawatha,
Empty-handed, heavy-hearted,
Heard Nokomis moaning, wailing:

"Wahonowin! Wahonowin!
Would that I had perished for you,
Would that I were dead as you are!
Wahonowin! Wahonowin!"
    And he rushed into the wigwam,
Saw the old Nokomis slowly
Rocking to and fro and moaning,
Saw his lovely Minnehaha
Lying dead and cold before him;
And his bursting heart within him
Uttered such a cry of anguish,
That the forest moaned and shuddered,
That the very stars in heaven
Shook and trembled with his anguish.
    Then he sat down, still and speechless,
On the bed of Minnehaha,
At the feet of Laughing Water,
At those willing feet, that never
More would lightly run to meet him,
Never more would lightly follow.
    With both hands his face he covered,
Seven long days and nights he sat there,
As if in a swoon he sat there,
Speechless, motionless, unconscious
Of the daylight or the darkness.
    Then they buried Minnehaha;
In the snow a grave they made her,
In the forest deep and darksome,
Underneath the moaning hemlocks;
Clothed her in her richest garments,
Wrapped her in her robes of ermine,
Covered her with snow, like ermine;
Thus they buried Minnehaha.
    And at night a fire was lighted,
On her grave four times was kindled,
For her soul upon its journey
To the Islands of the Blessed.
From his doorway Hiawatha
Saw it burning in the forest,
Lighting up the gloomy hemlocks;
From his sleepless bed uprising,
From the bed of Minnehaha,
Stood and watched it at the doorway,

That it might not be extinguished,
Might not leave her in the darkness.
  "Farewell!" said he, "Minnehaha!
Farewell, O my Laughing Water!
All my heart is buried with you,
All my thoughts go onward with you!
Come not back again to labor,
Come not back again to suffer,
Where the Famine and the Fever
Wear the heart and waste the body.
Soon my task will be completed,
Soon your footsteps I shall follow
To the Islands of the Blessed,
To the kingdom of Ponemah!
To the Land of the Hereafter!"

The Creation of Night

retold by Mercedes Dorson and Jeanne Wilmot

IN the beginning there was no night. Only daytime existed. There was sunshine and there were chirping birds and parrots, and mimosa flowers, and grasshoppers. But there were no crickets who sang through the dusk light nor were there night flowers like the beautiful *Victoria regia* whose petals spread at the suggestion of darkness. There was no sunset, no starlight, nor any night beasts. The jaguars, who only hunt in the night, did not yet live in the world where the people lived. The perfume of the delicate hanging orchids was burned by the bright heat of the ceaseless sunlight. There was no time to rest. Everywhere the sun and heat urged life on with no respite.

It happened that the Great Water Serpent who lived in the depths of the Madeira River had a beautiful daughter who possessed special powers. The daughter married a handsome man from a nearby village on the banks of the river. This man worked hard preparing his field and planting manioc, corn, and sweet potatoes. It saddened the daughter's heart when she saw her husband and his tribesmen toiling in the unending heat of the sun. He was a good man, and she loved him very much. During the harvest season, he would become so tired he would fall ill. But even though he would grow tired, he could not fall asleep because there was no night.

The sun made many beautiful things too vibrant to enjoy. Even the flaming macaw feathers worn as headdresses by the men were too bright for the Serpent's daughter. She grew to hate the sparkling river water that shimmered under the power of the baking sunlight. She was enraged, for she knew that a peaceful darkness called "Night" existed at the bottom of the river where her father had taken her once. Night was inhabited by all sorts of creatures, sounds, and phenomena. The Indians had never seen Night.

Finally, she cried out to her husband, "You must send someone to my father. He will bring us Night from the bottom of the river. He took me to see it once. There are nightsongs and peace in the cool darkness there. My husband, you will be able to sleep if there is Night. A calm, dark silence covers everything where it exists."

The man protested and told his wife, "My wife, I am afraid you are delirious from lack of sleep. There is only day."

But she exclaimed, "Night does exist! Send your servants to fetch Night!" The husband had no choice but to call three of his strongest and most loyal servants.

He told them, "You must go to the Great Water Serpent's house at the end of the large river and beg him to send me Night. Tell him his daughter wishes for the peace that will come with the darkness. And his daughter desires, too, the end to this exhaustion which will cease when Night comes and we are allowed to sleep. Tell the Serpent that his daughter's happiness depends on Night's arrival. Without it she will go mad."

And so the three servants set out. They boarded a canoe and traveled downriver. They paddled past the sandy cove where the crocodiles were basking in the sun and past the bend where the large fallen tree could be seen protruding from the water. Finally they found the Great Water Serpent curled up in his hammock, soundly asleep. The snake's hammock was woven from the fronds of the *miriti* palm and hung between two fallen trees on the bank of the river. The men quietly tied up their canoe and slowly approached the Serpent. He was a rowdy old spirit who had just feasted on a whole tapir whose carcass lay at the foot of the hammock. A cask of *caxiri*, a rum made of manioc flour, rested against his body. With difficulty the three tribesmen awakened the Great Serpent. At the moment his ungainly body stirred, they threw themselves at his feet.

"Who are you?" asked the Serpent. "And what do you want?"

"We implore you, Great Serpent, send Night back with us for your daughter. Your son-in-law labors long and hard, and yet he can never sleep. Your daughter hides from the light of day, always shielding her eyes. She grows sadder every day, and her husband worries that she might go mad."

The Serpent drew up from his prone position and spoke in a commanding voice. "You do not need to convince the father of a suffering child to end her suffering if it's within his power to do so. Wait here until I return."

The big snake descended to the bottom of the river. He was gone for over one hour. The three servants began to worry and commenced circling the area where he had disappeared. Finally he surfaced with a large fruit from the *tucumã* tree which looked like a big brown coconut. The Serpent handed the nut to the anxious men. The men noticed that a hole had been pierced on the top of the fruit and that the hole was now sealed with hardened resin.

As the immense snake handed the nut to the nervous men he warned them, "You must not open this nut or all will be lost. If the nut is cracked, everything will become dark. Only my daughter can manage the spirits of Night. When you return to my daughter, give her the nut and she will know what must be done."

That having been said, the Serpent curled himself back up into the hammock and waved to the loyal servants who departed immediately. The three servants boarded their canoe and started paddling their way home up the powerful river.

After the servants had been rowing a while, however, they began to hear strange noises coming from within the *tucumã* nut. The servants had never before heard such strange sounds. One of the servants suggested opening the nut. At first the other two did not agree. But soon new and peculiar sounds resonated inside the *tucumã* nut. *"Shay-Shay-Shay"* and *"Tem-Tem-Tem."* These sounds were followed by a medley of nightsongs. Full of curiosity and a small measure of fear, all three servants fell upon the nut and tore at its exterior. The noises became louder, and the night calls of the frogs, the crickets, and the *murucututús* soon overwhelmed the loyal servants. Their curiosity now was stronger than they could bear. The three men paddled their canoe to the shore and lit a small fire on the muddy banks of the river to melt the resin that closed the hole in the *tucumã* nut.

As soon as the hole opened, the sky turned black. The terrified servants could not see anything in the opaque air that surrounded them until the stars emerged from the hole. Once the starlight accumulated, they were astonished by the sight of the night animals flying out of the hole and invading the darkness with their eerie sounds. A swirl of creatures, moonbeams, and dew drops blew around the servants, transforming the texture of the very air they breathed.

In her sleeping hut many forests away, the daughter turned abruptly to her husband and said, "My father has given us the gift of Night and your servants have set it free."

The toads and small frogs began to croak. The owls and snipes started hooting. The *jurutai* birds, the *acuranas*, and the bats rushed out into the darkness, filling the forest with wailings and cries and night shrieks. The imprudent servants were dumbstruck.

The husband of the Great Water Serpent's daughter was terrified when he saw the basket that lay at the foot of his hammock transform into a jaguar with night eyes. The canoe on the river turned into a duck. The oar became a fish and the cord an anaconda. Everything in the rivers and the forest was transformed.

The man called out to his wife, "What shall we do? We must save daytime. All is lost!"

The woman pulled out a strand of her hair and told her husband, "Do not worry. With this strand I will separate Day and Night. I have no fear. Close your eyes and wait."

When the servants arrived, the husband, with closed eyes, reprimanded his men. The Great Water Serpent's daughter, who was an excellent sorceress, turned the men into monkeys for having disobeyed orders.

Meanwhile Night spun gleefully around the Water Serpent's daughter and her husband. Soon the husband fell asleep to the rhythms of the night beasts, the tree frogs, the crickets, and other night insects. Moonbeams lit the way for the newly born jaguar. Night owls hunted, and the gentle hum of bat wings comforted the daughter as she waited. She pushed aside the palm fronds at the entrance of their hut and the sweet night air her father had sent her streamed in, perfuming the darkness surrounding them. Soon, she, too, fell into a restful slumber. When she awakened, she used her strand of hair to gather up the ends of night which were scattered all over, and she forced them back into the *tucumã* nut. She picked up only part of the darkness, leaving some for people to use for sleeping and resting.

"Open your eyes, husband. Notice that dawn is coming and the birds are singing happily, announcing the arrival of the sun. And the night creatures have bedded down and are silent. The stars have disappeared into the sun's rays and the night petals of the *Victoria regia* flower are shut." From then on, Night took turns with Day so people could rest.

And so that is how Night was born.

The Seven Simeons

retold by James Riordan

ONCE upon a time there lived seven brothers, seven bold workingmen—all named Simeon.

One day, as they were in the fields greeting the sun at dawn, plowing the soil and sowing wheat, the king and his grandest noblemen came riding by. The king looked and, seeing the seven brothers, was much surprised.

"How can it be?" he said. "Seven lads plowing the field, all looking alike and of the same height too. Find out who they are."

The king's servants ran and brought back the seven Simeons.

"Tell me who you are and what you do," the king demanded. And the seven brothers replied:

"We are seven brothers, seven bold workingmen, and we are all called Simeon. We plow the land that was our father's and his father's before him. And each of us has a craft of his own."

"What, then, are your crafts?" asked the king.

Said the eldest brother:

"I am Simeon the Carpenter, and I can make a wooden column reaching to the sky."

Said the second brother:

"I am Simeon the Climber, and I can climb to the top of that column and look round the world."

Said the third brother:

"I am Simeon the Sailor, and I can build a ship in the wink of an eye, and sail her over the seas and under water, too."

"I am Simeon the Archer," said the fourth brother, "and I can hit a fly in the air with an arrow."

"I am Simeon the Star-Gazer," said the fifth brother, "and I can count the stars without missing a single one."

"I am Simeon the Plowman," said the sixth brother, "and I can plow a field, sow the grain and reap the harvest all in one day."

"And what can you do?" asked the king of the youngest of the seven Simeons.

"I can sing and dance, and play a flute," the lad replied.

At that, the king's counselor said scornfully:

"Workingmen we need, O King, good father, but what do we want of a fellow who can do nothing but dance and play! Send

141

him away, for such men are not worth the bread they eat or the water they drink."

"You are right," agreed the king.

At that, the youngest Simeon bowed to the king and said:

"Permit me to play for you and show what I can do."

"Very well," said the king, "play for me just once, then leave my kingdom!"

The youngest Simeon took out his pipe of birch and started playing. At once, everyone began to dance and skip and hop. The king danced, his nobles danced and the guards danced too. The horses frisked and capered, the cows in the sheds stamped in time to the music and, in the village, the hens and cocks hopped about gaily. But the king's counselor danced harder than anyone. In fact, so hard did he dance that the sweat rolled down his face, and the tears too, and his beard trembled and shook.

"Stop your playing! I can dance no longer, I am exhausted!" cried the king.

The youngest Simeon took the pipe from his lips and said:

"Rest now, good folk, all but you, counselor. You shall dance some more for your scornful tongue."

At once, everyone stood still, all but the counselor who went on dancing and could not stop. He danced and danced till at last his legs buckled beneath him and he sank to the ground utterly exhausted.

The youngest of the Simeons put away his pipe of birch and said:

"So, that, King, is my trade!"

The king laughed at this, but the counselor was ill pleased and plotted his revenge.

"Well now, Simeon the Eldest," said the king, "show us what *you* can do!"

And the oldest of the Simeons took an axe and made a wooden column reaching to the sky.

Then the second Simeon climbed to the top and began to look round the world.

"Tell us what you see!" the king called to him.

And the second Simeon called back,

"I see ships sailing upon the Seven Seas. I see wheat ripening in the fields."

"What else do you see?"

"On the Seventh Sea, I spy an island. It is the Isle of Buyan gleaming in the sun. And there, at the window of a golden palace, sits the Fair Tamara weaving a silken rug."

"What is she like? Is she really as beautiful as they say?" asked the king.

"That she is. Indeed, her beauty is greater than words can relate or tales unfold. Upon her head she wears a crescent moon and in her hair gleam lustral pearls."

Now this made the king eager to take the Fair Tamara for his wife; he was about to send his matchmakers when the sly counselor said:

"Why not send the seven Simeons for the Fair Tamara, O King, good father! They are skilful and strong; but, if they fail, you can chop off their heads."

"Yes, that's a good idea!" agreed the king.

So he ordered the seven Simeons to bring him the Fair Tamara.

"If you should fail," he warned, "I swear by my sword and my kingdom that your heads will roll from your shoulders."

There was nothing for it: Simeon the Sailor took an axe, and rap-a-tap-tap! he built a ship in the wink of an eye, fitted her out and rigged her too. They loaded the ship with goods of every sort and kind, and the king sent the costliest gifts he could command. He ordered his counselor to go with the brothers to see they did all they were told; the counselor was unhappy, but there was nothing for it.

They boarded the ship, and at her sides the billows lapped, in the wind the white sails flapped, and then they set sail across the Seven Seas to the Isle of Buyan that gleamed bright in the sun.

Whether they sailed for months or days nobody knows, but at last the island lay before them.

They stepped onto the shore, went straight to the Fair Tamara and, laying their costly gifts at her feet, told her of their mission.

She accepted the gifts, and, as she was unpacking them, the sly counselor whispered in her ear:

"Do not marry the king. He is old and feeble; in his kingdom wolves howl and bears prowl, black storms rage and white blizzards blow."

The Fair Tamara grew angry and ordered the matchmakers from her palace.

What were the seven brothers to do?

"Listen, my Brothers," said the youngest Simeon. "Board the ship and prepare to sail. Load it up with good fresh bread and leave it to me to fetch the Fair Tamara."

Before the hour was up, Simeon the Plowman had plowed up the sandy shore, sowed some rye, gathered in the harvest and baked enough bread to last a long voyage. They hoisted the sails and waited for the youngest Simeon.

Meanwhile Simeon went to the palace and stood beneath the window in which sat the Fair Tamara weaving a silken rug.

"It is so beautiful here," he said, "in the middle of the Seventh Sea, on the Isle of Buyan that gleams in the sunshine, but it is a hundred times more beautiful in Rus, my own dear land. Our rivers are blue and our birches are white; our fields are vast and our meadows are green and bright with flowers. In Rus, sunset meets sunrise as the moon keeps watch over the stars. Our dew is as sweet as honey, and our streams gleam like silver. In the morning, the shepherd goes into the green meadow and puts his birch-pipe to his lips and, whether you will it or not, you follow wheresoever he leads."

As soon as Simeon began playing on his pipe, the Fair Tamara stepped out of the golden palace. He crossed the palace's gardens and meadows with Tamara close behind. He walked on along the sandy shore and onto the ship with Tamara at his heels.

At once the brothers turned the ship round and set sail across the Seven Seas.

Simeon put down his pipe, and Tamara immediately woke up and looked about her. The Isle of Buyan gleaming bright in the sun was left far behind.

She threw herself upon the ship's pine floor and, turning into a bright star, streaked up into the sky and was lost in the heavens. But Simeon the Star-Gazer counted all the bright stars in the sky until he came upon the new star. Then Simeon the Archer loosed a golden arrow at the star, and it fell back to the ship and turned into the Fair Tamara.

The youngest Simeon told her:

"Do not try to run away, for there is nowhere you can hide from us. If you so dislike our company, we shall return you to your Isle of Buyan and let the king chop off our heads."

The Fair Tamara felt sorry for the brothers.

"No," she said, "he shall not chop off your heads because of me. You may take me to the king."

They continued their voyage across the Seven Seas. All the while the youngest Simeon never left the lovely princess and she gazed fondly upon him too.

But the sly counselor watched and laid his plans.

When they were nearing home and the shore was in sight, the counselor summoned the brothers out on deck and offered them each a goblet of sweet wine.

"Let us drink to our homeland, friends!" he said.

The brothers drank the wine, and stretching themselves out on the deck, fell into a deep sleep, for the counselor had put a sleeping potion in the wine; nothing could rouse the brothers, not thunder nor storm, not their mother's tears so tender and warm.

Only the Fair Tamara and the youngest Simeon, who had not touched the wine, stayed awake.

On reaching the shore, still the six brothers slept and Simeon made ready to take the Fair Tamara to the king. Both were sad, for it broke their hearts to part. But there was nothing for it: a promise must be kept.

Meanwhile the sly counselor hurried to the king and told him:

"O King, good father, the youngest Simeon intends to kill you and take the Fair Tamara for himself. Have him put to death."

Simeon presently appeared before the king with the Fair Tamara and was at once thrown into the deepest dungeon.

"Hear me, my Brothers, hear me, six Simeons!" he cried. "Come to my aid."

But the brothers slept on and did not wake.

At daybreak, Simeon was led out and taken to where the executioners were waiting.

The Fair Tamara wept, the tears rolling like pearls down her silver cheeks, but the sly counselor laughed.

Simeon spoke up before his death:

"O King, grant a last request before I die, for so our ancient custom bids you. Permit me to play my pipe one last time."

"Do not do so, O King, good father, do not let him play!" cried the counselor.

But the king replied:

"I cannot go against the custom of my fathers. Play, Simeon, but make haste, for my executioners have waited long enough; their sharp swords are becoming blunt."

Simeon put his birch-pipe to his lips and began to play.

Across hills and dales the music carried until it reached the ship where the six brothers slept and woke them up.

"Our youngest brother is in trouble!" they cried, leaping to their feet.

And off they rushed as fast as they could to the court.

The executioners had just raised their sharp swords and were about to chop off Simeon's head, when up raced the six brothers; Simeon the Carpenter, Simeon the Climber, Simeon the Plowman, Simeon the Sailor, Simeon the Star-Gazer and Simeon the Archer.

They moved in a body upon the old king and ordered him to free their young brother. Fearing for his life, the king released the youngest Simeon.

"Take the princess, too," he said hastily. "I do not like her anyway."

Soon after, the youngest Simeon and the Fair Tamara were married, and such a feast was held as the world had never seen. The guests drank and ate their fill, and sang merry songs with great goodwill.

Then the youngest Simeon took his pipe and began playing a merry tune.

The king danced, the princess danced, the grand nobles and their ladies danced too. The horses once more frisked and pranced, the cows in the sheds stamped in time to the music and, in the village, the hens and cocks hopped about gaily.

But the counselor danced harder than anyone. He danced and danced till his legs gave way under him and he fell down dead.

Once the wedding feast was over, it was time to get back to work.

And work they did!

Simeon the Carpenter built houses, Simeon the Plowman sowed wheat, Simeon the Sailor sailed the seas, Simeon the Star-Gazer kept a record of the stars, Simeon the Climber kept watch round the world and Simeon the Archer guarded Rus from her enemies. There is enough work for all in this great land of ours.

As for the youngest Simeon, he sang songs and played on his pipe, and his music warmed the people's hearts and lightened their labor.

Joongabilbil Brings Fire

edited by Barbara Ker Wilson

IN dhoogoorr times, Joongabilbil the Chicken Hawk was a seacoast man, and he was able to make fire by flapping his wings. No one else could make fire in those far-off days; all the people shivered in the cold seasons, and ate their meat raw, for they could not cook it.

Kart-gart, kart-gart, kart-gart: all the womba, the people who lived then, would hear the flapping of Joongabilbil's wings as he rose high, high in the sky, then swooped down to set the grass alight. The people would rush out to try to catch the fire while it was still burning, but it always went out before they could reach it.

One day, Joongabilbil lit a big marr-ju, a spreading bushfire, and went to the top of a tree to watch it. When the people saw this big fire, they ran out to try to catch it, as they always did, but even that big bushfire went out before they got there. Joongabilbil looked down from the top of the tree. He saw how the people shivered and shivered in the cold weather, and asked them, "Where is your fire? Why do you not make fire for youselves?"

"We do not know how to make it," the tribespeople told him. "That is why we shiver, and why we eat our meat raw."

When Joongabilbil heard this, he broke off some branches of the tree where he sat, and gave them to the people. Then he set the tree alight, and the people held their branches in the fire and took them away while they were still burning. And when they reached their own place, they were able to warm themselves and to cook their meat.

Joongabilbil watched them and saw that they no longer shivered, and he smelled the good smell of the meat that they cooked. Then he said, "I will put fire in the trees for always, so that you need never shiver or eat raw meat again." He put fire in the sandalwood tree, in the paperback tree, the mangrove, the blackboy, and many others as well, and he showed the people how to get fire by taking branches from these trees and twirling firesticks to kindle a blaze. And ever since that time the womba have kept the fire which Joongabilbil the Chicken Hawk gave them.

Biographical Notes

John R. Bailey (born 1940) Bailey was initially interested in folksinging as a hobby, which in turn led him to the study of myths and folklore and inspired his first writing. Born in England, he continues to live there with his wife, who is a music teacher, and two sons.

James Baldwin (1841–1925) Raised in an isolated Quaker community in Indiana, Baldwin had very little formal schooling. He was primarily self-taught and possessed an intense and wide-ranging love of reading. He was so well educated that at one time, half the schoolbooks in the United States were either edited or written by him.

Martin Bennett Bennett has widely researched the trickster character that appears often in African myth, including the spider/man Kweku Ananse, Tortie the Tortoise, and Leuk the Hare. Similar characters are often found in other parts of the world with different names: Luek is said to be related to the American folktale character Brer Rabbit. Of the trickster, Bennett says: "Part rogue, part pint-sized hero, he takes on the dubious laws of the jungle single-handed. What he lacks for in sheer bulk or strength, he makes up for in natural cunning."

Joseph Bruchac (born 1942) As a student, Bruchac (pronounced "brew-shack") worked as a laborer and tree surgeon. After graduation, he taught English literature in Ghana. His Native American perspective and his experience in Africa have taught him that all people share a common humanity, a trait he believes ". . . may be the one grace that can save us all."

Elsie Finnimore Buckley (born 1882) was a translator of several volumes of a French history series, published in the 1920's. The story in this volume is from her collection *The Children of the Dawn*, published in 1908. *The Children of the Dawn*, in spite of its title, was written for teenage readers and in its day had a following among romantically minded girls. It was also much used by storytellers.

Edgar Parin d'Aulaire (1898–1986) **Ingri d'Aulaire** (1904–1980) These Caldecott award-winning authors and illustrators have published so many distinguished books that their work has shaped children's literature during the twentieth century. Their writing has been translated into several languages and has been transcribed into Braille.

Mercedes Dorson Dorson was born and raised in Brazil. She has traveled in the Amazon region and spent time among the Brazilian Indians.

Michael Gibson Gibson is an internationally praised author and illustrator. He is best known for *Gods, Men and Monsters from Greek Myths*. He has also written *The Vikings* and several historical books.

Virginia Hamilton (born 1936) The descendant of enslaved African Americans, Virginia Hamilton has won many literary awards, including the Newbery Medal, the Laura Ingalls Wilder Medal, and the Edgar Allan Poe Award. She is a prolific writer who has published an average of one book a year since 1967.

Barbara Hayes (born 1944) Hayes has worked as an editor and writer in the field of children's literature for over thirty years. She has written more than sixty books. She travels widely and collects books of fairy tales, legends, folklore, and myths from around the world.

Max J. Herzberg (1886–1958) Herzberg was an educator who also wrote and edited numerous texts and anthologies. He exerted a strong influence on American secondary school programs by making literature a more significant presence in the curriculum. In addition, he was the literary editor of the *Newark Evening and Sunday News* for over 40 years and contributed widely to several periodicals.

Robert Ingpen (born 1936) Ingpen was born and lives in the State of Victoria in Australia. An illustrator, designer, printer, and writer, he has won many awards, including the Hans Christian Andersen Medal for his illustrations in the field of children's literature. Ingpen has written much about his native Australia, and he is known worldwide for *The Encyclopedia of Things That Never Were*. He has published many folklore books in collaboration with Barbara Hayes.

Barbara Ker Wilson (1929–1988) "I regard it as the universal well-spring of all imaginative writing," Ker Wilson says about folklore. She also sees children's literature as "a great force for international understanding." Originally from England, Ker Wilson moved to Australia, where her contact with the native Aborigineal people inspired her to retell their tales to an international audience.

Uma Krishnaswami Because she was born in northern India, lived for twenty years in Maryland, and now resides in the southwestern part of the United States, Krishnaswami believes that her home lies inside her. *The Broken Tusk: Stories of the Hindu God Ganesha* won the 1997 Scientific American Young Readers Book Award.

Maria Leach (1892–1977) Leach was one of America's best-known folklorists. She collected and edited the massive *Standard Dictionary of Folklore, Mythology and Legend,* diligently gathering thousands of previously scattered songs, proverbs, poems, riddles, and folktales.

Henry Wadsworth Longfellow (1807–1882) Longfellow, born in the seacoast town of Portland, Maine (then a part of Massachusetts), is among the most beloved American poets. His "Song of Hiawatha," published in 1855, is said to have sold one million copies during his lifetime. Longfellow based the character of Hiawatha on an actual 16th-century Mohawk chief, but the events of the poem are fictional.

Alice Low (Born 1926) Encouraged at school to "make books, puppets, and to write and act in plays," Low has written and produced filmstrips on folk songs and folklore. She has also written and published several popular books and operettas for children.

Olga Loya Master storyteller Loya is descended from Mexican American immigrants. Fluent in both English and Spanish, she moves seamlessly back and forth between the two languages to weave a bright, multicolored tapestry of folklore.

Dr. William Montgomerie (born 1904) A poet from Britain, Montgomerie has made many contributions to the study of Scottish culture. He published a book of Scottish nursery rhymes, contributed to the Review of Scottish Studies and to the Scottish Literary Journal. He received his Masters and Doctorate from Educational University of Glasgow and Edinburgh, and was editor for the Lines Review in Edinburgh.

Mary Pope Osborne Upon graduating from college, Osborne led a varied and independent life. She experienced travel in all parts of Europe and lived for six weeks in a cave on Crete. Her professions included working as a window dresser, an acting teacher, and a medical assistant before she turned to writing. In 1985, Osborne says, she "fell into mythology" and "never returned to 'real life.'"

Neil Philip Philip has written and edited more than thirty books. These include *The Tale of Sir Gawain, The Cinderella Story,* and *The Penguin Book of English Folktales.* Known for his interest in various forms of folklore and mythology, he has written *The Arabian Nights* as well as Native American books.

Ann Pilling A native of England, Pilling has written eleven novels for children, including the award-winning *Henry's Leg.* Her many short stories have also received high praise. She feels that a good story "begins in delight and ends in wisdom."

James Riordan (born 1936) As a boy Riordan read very little, although he had a vivid imagination. As he grew older, he became well-traveled and spent five years in Russia, where he gathered material for folktales.

Robert D. San Souci has worked at many jobs—bookstore manager, English teacher, and advertising copywriter—that brought him close to the world of words and writing.

Rosemary Sutcliff (1920–1992) Sutcliff is the author of many widely acclaimed historical novels for both children and adults. She has retold the legends of Beowulf and Tristan and Isolde, among others. Her Tristan and Isolde was a winner of the Boston Globe–Horn Book Award.

Nancy Van Laan Van Laan is the author of *Possum Come A Knockin',* a winner of the Parent's Choice Award and a best-selling picture book. Her collection of Native American poems and stories, *In a Circle Long Ago,* was an ALA Notable Book. Her works reflect her interest in the folklore of the Americas. She also has a particular fondness for the South of her childhood, where she remembers people sitting on the porch, eating home-cooked feasts, and telling stories far into the afternoon or evening. Van Laan feels that "No story is ever told twice in the same way."

Anne Terry White (1896–1980) Born in Russia, White wrote in English as well as in her native language. She adapted world masterpieces by Shakespeare, Sir Thomas Malory, and Robert Louis Stevenson.

Jeanne Wilmot is the author of *Dirt Angel,* a collection of short stories. Her work has won a number of prizes and appeared in many publications, including the *O. Henry Stories.*

Acknowledgments *(continued from p. ii)*

Dorling Kindersley Limited
"World Without Sun" from *The Illustrated Book of Myths* retold by Neil Philip. Copyright © 1995 Dorling Kindersley Limited, London. Text copyright © 1995 Neil Philip.

E. P. Dutton
From "The Sword in the Stone", by Rosemary Sutcliff from *The Sword and the Circle*, Copyright © 1981 by Rosemary Sutcliff.

Ecco Press
"The First People" and "The Creation of Night" from *Tales from the Rain Forest: Myths and Legends from the Amazonian Indians of Brazil* retold by Mercedes Dorson and Jeanne Wilmot. Copyright © 1997 by Mercedes Dorson and Jeanne Wilmot.

Faber and Faber Ltd.
From "The Wanderings of Aeneas", and "Echo and Narcissus" from *The Faber Book of Greek Legends* edited by Kathleen Lines. Copyright © Faber and Faber Ltd., 1973. All rights reserved.

Fulcrum Publishing, Inc.
"How Grandmother Spider Named the Clans" reprinted with permission from *Native American Animal Stories* told by Joseph Bruchac © 1992 Fulcrum Publishing, Inc., Golden, Colorado. All rights reserved.

Funk & Wagnalls, an imprint of K-III Reference Corp.
"From Bumba" from *The Beginning: Creation Myths Around the World* by Maria Leach. Copyright © 1956 by Funk & Wagnalls Company.

Harcourt Brace & Company
"Apsu and Tiamat the Creators" from *In the Beginning: Creation Myths From Around the World* told by Virginia Hamilton. Text copyright © 1988 by Virginia Hamilton.

Kestrel Books, Penguin Books Ltd.
"The Seven Simeons" from *Tales from Central Russia* retold by James Riordan. Text copyright © 1976 by James Riordan.

Kingfisher Books, an imprint of Larousse Kingfisher Chambers Inc.
"Persephone" from *Realms of Gold Myths & Legends from Around the World* by Ann Pilling. Text copyright © Ann Pilling 1993.

Alfred A. Knopf, Inc.
"Coyote and the Blackbirds" from *In a Circle Long Ago: A Treasury of Native Lore from North America* by Nancy Van Laan. Text copyright © 1995 by Nancy Van Laan.

Linnet Books/The Shoe String Press, Inc.
"The Broken Tusk" from *The Broken Tusk: Stories of the Hindu God Ganesha* retold by Uma Krishnaswami. Copyright © 1996 Uma Krishnaswami. Reprinted by permission of Linnet Books/Shoe String Press, Inc., North Haven, Connecticut.

Philomel Books, a division of The Penguin Putnam Publishing Group
"Hiiaka" from *Cut From the Same Cloth: American Women of Myth, Legend, and Tall Tale* by Robert D. San Souci. Text copyright © 1993 by Robert D. San Souci.

Scholastic, Inc.
"Chariot of the Sun God: The Story of Phaeton and Helios" from *Favorite Greek Myths* retold by Mary Pope Osborne. Text copyright © 1989 by Mary Pope Osborne. "The Death of Balder" and "Twilight of the Gods" from *Favorite Norse Myths* retold by Mary Pope Osborne. Text copyright © 1996 by Mary Pope Osborne. Reprinted by permission of Scholastic, Inc.

Acknowledgments

Scribner, a division of Simon & Schuster, Inc.
"Brunhild" from *The Story of Siegfried* by James Baldwin. Copyright 1882, 1888, 1931 by Charles Scribner's Sons. Copyright 1910 by James Baldwin.

Simon & Schuster Books For Young Readers, an imprint of Simon & Schuster Children's Publishing Division
"Mother Earth and Her Children," "Zeus and the Creation of Mankind," and "Perseus" Reprinted with the permission of Simon & Schuster Books for Young Readers, an imprint of Simon & Schuster Children's Publishing Division, from *The Macmillan Book of Greek Gods and Heroes* by Alice Low. Copyright © 1985 by Macmillan Publishing Company.

A. P. Watt
"Krishna and the Serpent" from *Gods and Men: Myths and Legends from the World's Religions,* retold by John Bailey, Kenneth McLeigh, David Spearman. Copyright © John R. Bailey, Kenneth McLeigh, David Spearman 1981.

Western Publishing Company, Inc.
"Daedalus", "Theseus and the Minotaur", and "The Golden Fleece" adapted from *The Golden Treasury of Myths and Legends by* Anne Terry White. Copyright © 1959 Western Publishing Company, Inc.

Note: Every effort has been made to locate the copyright owner of material reprinted in this book. Omissions brought to our attention will be corrected in subsequent editions.